What to Do
When the Numbers
Are In

What to Do When the Numbers Are In

A User's Guide to Statistical Data Analysis
in the Human Services

Joan W. DiLeonardi, Ph.D.

Patrick Almond Curtis, Ph.D.

Nelson-Hall nh Chicago

Project Editor: Richard Meade
Designer: Claudia von Hendricks
Copy Editor: Barbara Armentrout
Typography: Precision Typographers

Library of Congress Cataloging-in-Publication Data

DiLeonardi, Joan.
  What to do when the numbers are in.

  Bibliography: p.
  Includes index.
  1. Social service—Statistical methods.   I. Curtis,
Patrick Almond.   II. Title.
  HV29.D54   1988   3619.00195195   87-25537
  ISBN 0-8304-1145-3

Manufactured in the United States of America

10   9   8   7   6   5   4   3   2

™ The paper used in this book meets the minimum requirements of American National Standard for Information Sciences—Permanence of Paper for Printed Library Materials, ANSI Z39.48-1984.

For Mary and Kurt

CONTENTS

LIST OF TABLES

LIST OF FIGURES

INTRODUCTION

This book is for college students or service-delivery people with an interest in applied research and usable knowledge. It is intended for (1) the relatively inexperienced researcher embarking on a first substantial project and (2) the experienced researcher who wants to enhance the usage of statistical data analysis. It should be helpful whether or not you use a computer to process your information. We assume that you, the reader, have some familiarity with research concepts and design, but just to make sure we are all talking about the same things, we intend to take every opportunity to review the basic terms that are essential for building expertise in data analysis.

Maybe you work as a program administrator or researcher in the human services. You may have done research before, but now you are about to tackle a program evaluation or social survey using more rigorous standards than you needed to employ in the past. Maybe you are a master's or doctoral student faced with producing a fairly sophisticated thesis or dissertation. Whatever your circumstances, the subjects of your study are people, in all their infinite variety.

We will present an approach that is reasonable and logical. We believe in procedures that are supported by sound argument. Our hope is that we can all learn to use numbers proficiently and in a manner that illuminates rather than detracts from what we can learn about people.

Our framework for data analysis consists of the following steps.

1. Planning the study

2. Getting started
3. Describing the data
4. Bivariate relationships
5. Establishing reliability
6. Multivariate relationships

Notice that we have created our own *Heart of Darkness*. The further one proceeds, the more complicated (and the more interesting) the analysis becomes. This structure is purposive. We want this user's guide to be helpful to the beginner and the experienced alike. You can choose where to begin the book and how far you want to take your data through these steps.

The book is intended to be a reference guide. You will probably not have to read it from cover to cover. You can pick and choose and refer back to those sections that you need for your particular data analysis. Perhaps you have forgotten what parametric statistics are. This guide is designed to review such things easily. Perhaps you need to do something more difficult than you ordinarily do, like identify the multiple causes of program or treatment outcome. The chapters on multivariate techniques are there for that purpose. Like the chapters on single variate and bivariate analysis, they are intended to teach what the techniques are used for, how to assess whether your data are appropriate for such statistics, how to choose the correct procedure, and how to interpret the results.

ACKNOWLEDGEMENTS

We would like to thank several people associated with our publisher, Nelson-Hall: Beulah R. Compton, consulting editor for social welfare, Ronald F. Warncke, and Stephen Ferrara, for advice and encouragement; Kristen Westman, Dorothy Anderson, and Richard Meade for editorial assistance. Thanks also to Leroy H. Blumenthal for providing us with the pie charts.

CHAPTER 1

Planning and the Enhancement of Statistical Data Analysis

There are essentially four areas in which planning for a data analysis can enhance the power of your results. These decisions include (1) whether or not to use a computer, (2) the sample size or number of subjects in the study, (3) the method used in selecting or assigning subjects for study, and (4) levels of measurement. This chapter will orient you to each of these four crucial considerations.

First, an additional word about planning. Careful planning at the beginning of the study makes data analysis much easier at the end of it. It may even save your project by enabling you to account for unexpected results from information you thought to be relatively unimportant at the beginning of your study. Any veteran of several research projects has horror stories of recognizing too late that an additional question should have been asked, or that a question should have been asked in a different manner or of different people in order to provide clear results. Planning is the way to avoid horror stories of your own.

There are several major things to consider in the initial planning stages; among them are how you are going to analyze your data, who is going to do it, and how much time you have.

1

1.1 Manual or Computerized Analysis?

Probably the most basic practical consideration is whether you have access to a computer and the knowledge to use it for statistical analysis. If all your data tallying and manipulation are going to be done by hand, your procedures will be quite different than if you have both computer access and expertise. The sheer tediousness of hand manipulation of large quantities of data means that you will spend a great deal of time and money for clerical help unless you simplify the project as much as possible. Also, the necessary repeated hand tallying of large amounts of data can lead to a high number of errors. This does not mean that you are limited to asking only name, rank and serial number. But it does mean that, contrary to most of the advice in this book, it will be necessary for you to categorize the data for easy tabulation, to keep the categories small, discrete, and simple, and to content yourself with describing the data in terms of summary counts and percentages and looking at relationships between only two characteristics at a time.

Now if you believe, as we do, that people are not one- or two-dimensional and that the human beings we study come in infinite varieties, then one- or two-dimensional analyses cannot be very interesting. And even if such an analysis is interesting, it still may not be sufficient.

Seemingly obvious relationships may be misleading. Underlying characteristics often provide at least partial explanations for seemingly straightforward relationships. For example, there might be a strong relationship between height and playing football in high school, that is, football players tend to be tall. Is height the only cause of playing high school football? It is easy to speculate that gender, strength, parental influence, social customs at the time of high school attendance, as well as interest in body-contact sports might affect participation in high school football to the same extent as height. Indeed, it could be argued that several of these are more important than height in determining the act or level of participation. Doing analysis by hand, or with a calculator, one could look at the relationship between each one of these phenomena and participation in high school football. This would probably result in finding that there are strong relationships between several of these characteristics and participation. But there is really no way to determine to what extent football playing is explained by the relative effects of height, strength, and interest without using multivariate statistics. Since most of this class of statistics involve complex and tedious matrix manipulation, both the time and the possibility of errors caused by the repetition argue for the use of a computer. Computers excel in boring repetitions and do them faster and more accurately than most human beings.

Let's take an example from the human services. Suppose the staff of a therapeutic day care center wants to use play therapy with a group of developmentally delayed toddlers, and they want to measure the effectiveness of their treatment in helping the children master appropriate developmental tasks. By applying some standardized criteria of child behavior, they might discover a strong positive relationship between play therapy and development. But how will they know whether other contributors might not be equally or more important, such as normal growth, especially if the children are only two or three years old, a time of relatively rapid maturation? The resources needed to sort out such a configuration statistically are substantial and, realistically, require a computer.

If you do not have access to a computer or sufficient knowledge to use it for this kind of analysis, you would be sensible to restrict yourself to the kind of analysis done 20 or so years ago before the advent of high-speed, low-cost computer data analysis software. This involves calculating how much human computing and coding time you can afford and restricting your study to what you can reasonably do with those resources. This probably means that characteristics such as age, income, years of schooling, and scores on standardized tests will have to be collapsed into manageable categories that make sense in light of the questions you want answered. If you are doing a study of user perceptions of a school-based program, it might not be feasible to maintain separate categories for every variation in age. As an alternative, consider the categories birth to 5 years, 6 years to 10 years, 11 years to 15 years, and so on. School grade might be categorized as freshman and sophomore for your first category and junior and senior for your second.

If you were questioning young adults or senior citizens, the categories would be different, based on what groupings seem to be meaningful in the light of your purpose. If you are calculating the results by hand, unless there is a large staff involved, you cannot realistically and accurately handle more than 75 to 100 cases from which you have collected information derived from a three- or four-page questionnaire. The calculations themselves could take more than a week or two. If you have several questionnaires or a lot of background data, you may want to restrict yourself to studying 30 to 50 people. If data for your study can be completed on a one-page questionnaire, you may be able to handle information on 150 or 200 people with hand analysis if the questions are mostly closed-ended and precoded, but don't underestimate the amount of time required just to understand the data and look for meaningful relationships.

The use of the terms *closed-ended* and *precoded* may need a little discussion. A closed-ended question is one in which the person responding can only choose from among answers already determined and presented to him. Precoded questions are those for which the possible responses and their numerical values have already been determined. *Open-ended questions* usually provide space for the respondent or interviewer to write a narrative or

The Closed-Ended Question

Have you ever recommended day care services to a friend?
(Please circle one response only.)

Yes 1

No 0

The Open-Ended Question

If you have recommended day care, describe one example.

_____

_____

_____

_____

FIGURE 1.1   Examples of Closed- and Open-Ended Questions

make notes. See Figure 1.1 for examples of closed-ended and open-ended questions.

Many times people associate closed-ended questions with the use of computers, and it is true that it is much easier and cheaper to have a coder or data-entry clerk take your questionnaires and enter the data onto the computer than it is to have someone more skilled and knowledgeable in the subject of the study interpret the answers to each open-ended question. It is also undeniably true that if you are hand-manipulating data, it is easier to make ticks or hatch marks on a tally sheet if, without interpretation, you know in what category the answer belongs. In either case, the optimum way of collecting data is probably to have the majority of your questions precoded and closed-ended, with additional open-ended questions requiring explanatory answers in areas that are especially important or require interpretation.

These open-ended answers then need to be classified in some way, either for your hand tally sheet or for the computer. The text of the comments can be used for illustration, enhancement, and clarification of your findings. Since it is as true for researchers as for other human beings that the most poignant, cogent, and/or recent comment often assumes disproportionate importance in memory, open-ended answers should be organized in some way before tallying. The simplest and often the most effective way is to develop a matrix with the case numbers down a vertical column on the left and the question numbers in a horizontal row across the top. In this way one person's answers to all open-ended questions can be compared by reading across, or all respondents' answers to one question can be compared by reading down. Although this takes some organizing initially, it can be a real time-saver when writing your final report and can help you not to overemphasize an especially well-written but idiosyncratic response.

1.2 Sample Size and Selection

Sample size and sample selection are the second and third areas in which planning can enhance the power of your analysis. How many people or cases you are going to study (*sample size*) and how you are going to decide which ones they are (*sample selection*) help determine what techniques of data analysis you can legitimately use and how far you can generalize results beyond the subjects you have studied. If your sample size is adequate and your sample has been representatively selected from a larger population, you can legitimately claim that your findings tell you something about that larger group.

1.2.1 Sample Size

An adequate sample size increases the probability that your findings represent reality. The size of the group you are studying also determines what data analysis techniques you can use legitimately without being either unprofessional or misleading. First, too small a sample can lead to unprofessionalism. Workers who would never dream of betraying their clients' confidences or gossiping about them publicly may inadvertently do so because they are not aware of the necessity to disguise people's identity in statistical descriptions of small samples. If your study describes one worker's caseload of ten special-needs adoption cases, such as those in Table 1.1, including the twelve-year-old girl, Cheri, who has a history of fire-setting under stress and who was adopted by an upper-middle-class single woman, you may well have told half the community personal details that they didn't know but can identify now by connecting what they did know with your data.

Although there are statistics that can be used with very small groups of people, a sample of about 30 is the minimum considered necessary for statistical stability. Too much distortion results with fewer numbers. If the group you are studying is very small and you do not wish to generalize to some larger population, it may be more advantageous to forego a statistical analysis and describe the group qualitatively.

If 30 is the practical minimum, is that enough in all cases? The answer to that is obviously no, since, if you want to draw conclusions about all the teenaged parents in one state, you would need more subjects than if you wanted to generalize about the parents in one high school. If you were studying the 11,000 children in foster care in one state, a sample of 30 probably would not be adequate to support any generalizations you might want to infer, but a sample of 200 might be. The minimum sample size of about 30 is then only a rough lower estimate for the utilization of most statistical techniques.

There are formulas for computing adequate sample size in order to maximize the power of a given statistical test

TABLE 1.1 Average Age of Special-Needs Children

Name	Age	Handicapping Condition
Susie	1	Cerebral palsy
Janet	2	Sibling group
Johnny	3	Sibling group
Mark	7	Sibling group
Michael	2	None
Sammy	2	Down's syndrome
Cheri	12	Fire-setting
Louise	2	Visually impaired
Harry	2	Developmentally delayed
Matt	2	Failure to thrive

(Cohen 1979). There are also tables based on the use of sampling principles and experience that relate sample size to generalizability (Krijcie and Morgan 1970). If you have access to computer time and statistical software, the maximum sample size may be whatever you have as resources to code, process, and analyze.

1.2.2 Sample Selection and Sample Assignment

By *sample selection,* we mean choosing the subjects for study. By *sample assignment,* we mean assigning subjects to specific conditions.

Before continuing, we must say a few words about research design (which is like saying a few words about the *Oxford English Dictionary*). There are many ways of studying people with statistics, and they have been formulated and described in many places, but, essentially, you can either conduct a survey (i.e., poll your subjects in person, by mail, or over the telephone), or you can conduct a field experiment (i.e., measure the effects of some intervention or treatment). In a survey, it is necessary to *select* subjects for study. In a field experiment, it is necessary to *assign* subjects to certain conditions, usually an intervention/treatment group and a control/comparison group.

The ideal method of sample selection or sample assignment—and the one that meets the assumptions of (and, therefore, allows the use of) the more powerful statistical techniques—is *random selection* or *random assignment.*

The procedure for obtaining a random sample depends on the research design. In random sampling for surveying and polling, each subject has an equal chance of being included in the study. The purpose is to ensure that the study subjects reflect the personal characteristics, demographics, or attitudes of all the people from which they were drawn. In a true random sample, all the names or other identifiers of the potential subjects, or the *population,* are figuratively put into a "hat" and blindly chosen one by one until there are enough subjects for the study. Every time a subject is chosen, the name goes back into the "hat" and, therefore, can be chosen again. This is called *random sampling with replacement.*

It is possible that the same subject may be selected more than once. Purists will allow this to occur. We would prefer, however, that a subject not receive more than one phone call or one questionnaire in the mail. Therefore, once chosen, the name stays out of the "hat." This is called *random sampling without replacement.*

In a field experiment, it may not be necessary to select subjects from a larger population. You are more likely to have access to the entire population you have chosen for study. For example, you may want to test an innovative mode of treatment such as family therapy on a group of adolescents with substance-abuse problems. After identifying all the appropriate cases in your agency or clinic, you might decide that half the cases will receive family therapy, the other half more traditional, individual psychotherapy. In this example, the purpose of randomly assigning the cases into one group or the other is not to assure representativeness, but *equivalency*. In other words, the groups should be the same, technically speaking, not different, at the beginning of the experiment so that differences in outcomes can be attributed to the differences in interventions.

In random assignment, each subject has an equal chance of being assigned to the alternative conditions. It is not possible, however, to randomly assign a subject into a group that receives a particular service or treatment and then randomly assign that same case into a comparison group that either receives no service or receives an alternative service. So once a subject is assigned, he or she is removed from the "hat" or potential pool of subjects. This is called *random assignment without replacement*.

Any one of a number of valid random sampling techniques may be used in either design. If your population list is in alphabetical order, unless you have some reason to believe that people at the beginning of the alphabet are systematically different in some way from those in the middle or at the end, you can simply choose every nth case for your sample. If you are doing a needs assessment of 1,000 people from an alphabetical membership list of a senior citizens' organization and have decided that 100, or one-tenth, is an adequate sample, you can simply count down the list and place every tenth name in your sample. However, if the purpose of your needs assessment is to help make the choice among developing a meals-on-wheels program, a senior day care center, or a recreational trip program, choosing subjects from a list of those who have attended senior trips to baseball games and bingo parties would probably introduce a substantial bias in favor of more active programs. If you are assigning cases to two or more groups in a field experiment, you can consult a table of random numbers or flip a coin.

Statistical techniques make no judgments regarding the validity of your sampling method or representativeness of your subjects. The most inadequate and unrepresentative data can be fed into a computerized statistical package or a hand-held calculator and give you a numerical answer that purports to show the strength and statistical significance of a relationship. Because of this, the job of data analysis begins with planning your study, particularly the sample size and selection methods that enhance the validity and usefulness of your results. Levels of measurement, as we will see next, are also something you plan for.

1.3 Levels of Measurement

You may have read about levels of measurement so many times that you are wondering why we are presenting it here. First, we want to present these important concepts in the manner that we have found best explains them. Second, we want to demonstrate how levels of measurement can be manipulated for purposes of increasing the power of your analysis.

There are essentially four *levels* or *scales of measurement:* nominal, ordinal, interval, and ratio. These important concepts were first codified by S. Stevens in an article titled "On the Theory of Scales of Measurement" (1946).

Levels of measurement refer to a variable's quantitative potential. First of all, what is a variable? A *variable* is a characteristic that varies. *Age* is a variable because it is a characteristic that can have many values; in this case, it can vary from one individual to another. The concept *book* and the color *yellow* in and of themselves are not variables unless *book* refers to, for example, various kinds of books such as fiction and nonfiction. Similarly, *yellow* can be a variable if it encompasses varying shades of yellow.

It is crucial to understand the difference between discrete and continuous variables. A *discrete variable* is a variable in which the individual values are mutually exclusive, and, more importantly, one in which the intervals between values, or the *class intervals,* cannot be mea-

Types of Social Service Settings

Mental Health Clinic
Child Welfare Agency
Community Action Center
Other

FIGURE 1.2   Example of a Discrete Variable

sured. An example is the variable Types of Social Service Settings in Figure 1.2.

In this example the values are simply categories. It is useful to think of the variable Types of Social Service Settings as a *scale* of values despite, in this example, the lack of any ranked order. The values or categories of any scale must be (1) exhaustive, or, in other words, include all possible categories of Types of Social Service Settings, and (2) mutually exclusive, that is, each category must be unique and not, as far as possible, overlap with the other categories.

Types of Social Service Settings is a discrete variable because the class interval cannot be measured between its values. One cannot measure the distance between, for example, Mental Health Clinic and Child Welfare Agency. Although there may be similarities between mental health clinics and child welfare agencies, there cannot be a "Mental Health Clinic and a half" or a "Child Welfare Agency point six."

A *continuous variable* is a variable in which the class intervals can be measured, in fact, infinitely measured, and one in which the class intervals are of equal size. For instance, some people can run 100 meters in 11 seconds, a few can run 100 meters in 10 seconds, and it is also possible to run 100 meters in 10.5 seconds or in 10.55667 (and so on) seconds. The class interval between 10 seconds and 11 seconds can be measured in infinite gradations, and the distance between 10 and 11 seconds and 11 and 12 seconds is equal. Therefore, Time in Running 100 Meters is a continuous variable. Age, income, hourly wages, and grade-point average are other kinds of continuous variables. In fact, so is any variable where the values can be averaged.

If you can understand the important difference between these two kinds of variables, you will have little difficulty with levels of measurement. Levels of measurement will also help you understand statistical assumptions and the differences between *nonparametric* (those that make no assumptions about the normal distribution of underlying data), and *parametric* (those that can be used to make inferences about a larger population) statistics. A knowledge of those important concepts will allow you to select the most appropriate and most powerful statistical tests for your analysis.

As we will see below, nominal and ordinal scales are comprised of discrete variables. Interval and ratio scales are comprised of continuous variables.

1.3.1 Nominal-Level Measurement

Nominal, from the Latin, meaning "of or belonging to a name," refers to scales that are scales *in name only.* The scales are actually made up of lists of discrete categories. Our variable Types of Social Service Settings is an example of nominal-level measurement. The values Mental Health Clinic, Child Welfare Agency, Community Action Center, and Other comprise a scale in name only, consisting of categories in which the class intervals cannot be measured.

1.3.2 Ordinal-Level Measurement

Ordinal-level scales also contain discrete categories in which the class intervals are unknown and not measurable. However, an *ordering principle* is involved (both *or-*

Client Evaluation of Service

Very Poor
Poor
Fair
Good
Excellent

FIGURE 1.3 Example of an Ordinal-Level Variable

der and *ordinal* come from the Latin for "arrangement or group"). The scales progress from the lowest to the highest value or the highest to the lowest value. Suppose we ask clients to rate their experience in receiving service from a social agency. We might ask them to evaluate their experience from very poor to excellent, as in Figure 1.3. The possible responses are ordered, but the individual values remain discrete. We cannot, for instance, measure the distance between Poor and Fair or know whether the distance between Fair and Good equals the distance between Good and Excellent.

Ordinal scales are more powerful than nominal scales. For statistical purposes, there is more information contained in the ordering than there is in categorical lists.

1.3.3 Interval-Level Measurement

Interval-level variables or scales are ordered and continuous. The class intervals are of equal length, but the scales lack an absolute zero point. Because the class intervals can be measured—which is possible because the variables are continuous—they are more powerful than ordinal level variables.

A good example of interval-level data from the social sciences is standardized test scores such as the I.Q. Scores are frequently averaged, but no proportional statements can be made logically. For instance, an individual with an

I.Q. of 150 is not necessarily one and one-half times as smart as an individual with an I.Q. of 100. No absolute zero point exists, because it is not possible to have an I.Q. of zero.

An often-used example of an interval scale is the thermometer. The individual values or degrees are ordered and, because the difference between one degree and another can be measured by the strength of heat in causing mercury to rise or fall, the class intervals can be measured. It is therefore, possible to obtain a value of 90 degrees, 91 degrees, 50.5 degrees, 50.567 degrees, and so on. In addition, the value 50.5 degrees, for example, has a specific meaning. It is exactly halfway between 50 and 51 degrees. However, it is often stated that thermometers have arbitrary rather than absolute zero points because neither 0 degree Fahrenheit nor 0 degree centigrade means the absolute absence of heat. That doesn't necessarily mean, however, that the scales lack an absolute zero point. One can argue that the value zero is merely in the wrong place, which means that thermometers are ratio-level rather than interval-level scales.

1.3.4 Ratio-Level Measurement

Like interval level data *ratio-level scales* are ordered and the class intervals are measurable and of equal distance. In addition, ratio-level scales have logical and absolute zero points. For example, for the variable Income, it is possible to have a value of zero, or no income. For the variable Number of Appointments with a Caseworker, it is logically possible not to have seen the caseworker. The absolute zero point allows one to make "ratio" or proportional statements. An income of $20,000 is twice as large as an income of $10,000. Someone who has had 15 appointments has had three times the appointments as someone who has had 5.

TABLE 1.2 Client Continuance and Client Hope That Problems Could Be Solved

		Distribution of Ratings		
		Original Study		*Replication Study*
Degree of Hope	*N*	*Client Continued (%)*	*N*	*Client Continued (%)*
High	156	86 (55.0%)	37	21 (56.8%)
Moderate	157	50 (31.8%)	255	137 (53.7%)
Low	38	8 (21.1%)	87	30 (34.4%)
Total	351		379	

As mentioned previously, one cannot make proportional statements with interval-level data. It does not make sense to say that a person with a grade-point average of 1.00 did one-third as well as the student with a 3.00 grade-point average.

Except for this ability to use ratio comparisons, there is no difference between interval- and ratio-level data for statistical purposes. We can use the same statistics with interval-level data, both descriptive and inferential, that we can with ratio-level data.

For a quick summary of what we have said about levels of measurement, consult Table 1.2.

1.4 Levels of Measurement and Statistical Power

Levels of measurement do not float somewhere waiting to be discovered. We can plan for and make any data we collect into interval-level data and, therefore, increase the *power* of our analysis. By *power* we mean the ability of data to represent reality. Later when we present levels of measurement in terms of statistical relationships, you will understand how power relates to the ability of a statistical test to reveal relationships among variables. Often data is collected at lower levels of measurement than necessary

Age	
Under 25	1
26–34	2
35–44	3
45–54	4
55–64	5
65 and over	6

FIGURE 1.4 Statistical Power and Grouped Data: Example 1

for no apparent reason. We will show you some examples of this practice and how to avoid doing it.

In Figure 1.4, we can see that analysis can lose power when data is collected in groups. Age is a somewhat unusual variable in that values are rounded to the next lowest age. A person who is 26 years and 8 months old is reported to be 26 years old even though that person is closer to 27 years old. Because this rounding principle was not taken into consideration, the scale in Figure 1.4 has no category for a person 25 years old. (The numbers on the right represent codes for computer processing.) The first category is for those under 25, and one has to be 26 to fit into the second category.

In this case statistical power has been lost because of uneven *class widths.* In the category 26–34, the class width is nine years (26 years through 34 years and 364 days). In the category 35–44, the class width is ten years (35 years through 44 years and 364 days). Respectively, the class widths for all categories are 25 years, 9 years, 10 years, 10 years, 10 years, and unknown years. Therefore, potential ratio-level data has been reduced to ordinal-level data.

In order to strengthen your data collection, we recommend that you simply ask people how old they are. If you want to group the data, say, for purposes of describing the

What was your total household income last year from all sources, before taxes? I will read some income ranges, and you just tell me whether it was in that range or not.

A.	Was it between $5,000 and $10,000, above that range, or below it?	Below $5,000 .01 $5,000–10,000 .02 Above $10,000.....(ask B)
B.	Was it between $10,000 and $20,000	Yes . . . . .03 No . . . .(ask C)
C.	Was it between $20,000 and $25,000	Yes . . . . .04 No . . . .(ask D)
D.	Was it between $25,000 and $30,000	Yes . . . . .05 No . . . .(ask E)

FIGURE 1.5 Statistical Power and Grouped Data: Example 2

ages of your respondents, you can then carve up the data any way you wish.

If you collect grouped data, at least make the class widths equal.[1] This could not be done with the questions from a telephone survey in Figure 1.5. The responses will be ordinal-level data although the information is derived from the ratio-level variable Income.

Again, it would be better to simply ask people how much money they earn in one year. However, if you think that giving people the choice of responding to ranges will reduce the amount of missing information, you can at least make the class widths even, as in Figure 1.6. Notice that we have allowed 5 columns for the computer (in this example arbitrarily numbered 51–55). The responder answers 4, for example, but the researcher enters 17,500 into the computer (the mid-point value of class 4). With a large

---

[1]Equal class widths would not assume the same importance if the data analysis were conducted manually.

			51–55
Less than $4,999	1	$25,000 to 29,999	6
$5,000 to 9,999	2	$30,000 to 34,999	7
$10,000 to 14,999	3	$35,000 to 39,999	8
$15,000 to 19,999	4	$40,000 or more	9
$20,000 to 24,999	5		

FIGURE 1.6 Grouped Data and Ratio-Level Measurement

enough *N* (which is the symbol for number of cases), the responses within each class will be randomly distributed. This allows the researcher to average the responses because ratio-level data for income was retained.

1.4.1 Enhancing the Power of Nominal-Level Data

The *none/some scale* is a special case of nominal-level data. It is *dichotomous,* containing only two categories. One category is assigned a value of 1 and represents the presence of some characteristic: the other category is assigned a value of 0 and represents the absence of that same characteristic. Recall the variable Types of Social Service Settings. Suppose we are especially interested in the mental health clinics. Instead of constructing a scale with the values (1) Mental Health Clinic, (2) Child Welfare Agency, (3) Community Action Center, and (4) Other, we could construct the none/some scale in Figure 1.7.

The categories have been collapsed into a dichotomous scale with the values of (1) Mental Health Clinic, and (0) Other. Technically, the categories are (1) Mental Health Clinic, and (0) Not a Mental Health Clinic.

Types of Social Service Settings	
Mental Health Clinic	1
Other	0

FIGURE 1.7 The None/Some Scale

Types of Social Service Settings	
Mental Health Clinic	1
Other	0

Types of Social Service Settings	
Child Welfare Agency	1
Other	0

Types of Social Service Settings	
Community Action Center	1
Other	0

FIGURE 1.8 Multiple None/Some Scales

None/some scales are, technically speaking, nominal-level scales that are treated as ratio-level data because (1) they contain a known order, that is, from 0 to 1, (2) they contain a known class interval, that is 1, and (3) there is an absolute zero point.

It is also possible to transform a single nominal-level variable into several none/some scales. These are often referred to as *dummy variables.* For example, the variable Types of Social Service Settings can be transformed into three variables as seen in Figure 1.8. The usefulness of dummy variables will be explained in subsequent chapters on multivariate techniques.

Optimally, one can create up to k–1 variables, that is, one less than the number of categories. Creating one variable for *each* category would cause some cases to be represented twice.

1.4.2 Enhancing the Power of Ordinal-Level Data

Ordinal-level data can be used as interval data by simply assuming that the class intervals are equal. This is done

Client Evaluation of Service								
Very Poor	1	2	3	4	5	6	7	Excellent

FIGURE 1.9 Example of a Likert Scale

frequently in the social sciences, particularly with the *Likert scale*. Respondents are asked to rate something on a scale from 1 to *N*. Sometimes each possible response is given a descriptor, and sometimes not, as in Figure 1.9.

Sometimes such scales have an even number of values, which forces the respondent to choose a value on the negative or positive half of the scale. Our preference is to use an odd number of responses, usually no more than seven, that seem balanced by providing the respondent with a neutral choice. Such a choice would be the value 4 in Figure 1.9. The balance could be emphasized further by scaling the values from –3 to + 3 instead of 1 to 7.

The above scale is ordered and there is no absolute zero point, because value of zero does not mean a complete lack of opinion. Thus, the scale is not ratio level. Is the scale continuous? Is the distance between values equal and measurable? Technically, no. However, it is the commonly accepted practice to assume that the class intervals in Likert scales are equidistant and continuous, and, therefore, are interval-level data.

Well, you might ask, what is the difference in levels of measurement between the Likert scale and the scale

Very Poor/Poor/Fair/Good/Excellent

that was used previously as an example of an ordinal scale? In our opinion, there is no important difference, but only under certain circumstances can ordered data be assumed to be interval level.

There are two procedures that we think have merit. The first entails evaluating the ability of the data to predict an outcome. The second entails comparing the results of nonparametric statistical tests with parametric tests. Both procedures attempt to substantiate that ordered categories represent measurable differences, that is, real as opposed to arbitrary numbers. If that can be achieved, we think that the assumption of interval-level data is justified.

An example of the first procedure is taken from a well-known clinical study. In the mid-1950s Lillian Ripple and her colleagues conducted a series of studies that investigated the ability of three constructs, motivation, capacity, and opportunity, to predict client use of casework services (Ripple, 1955; Ripple, Alexander, and Polemis, 1964). One important element of motivation was hope. Each client's degree of hopefulness was assessed on a five-point scale as seen in Figure 1.10.

In two separate studies, it was found that a high degree of hope was associated with continuance in casework and that a low degree of hope was associated with discontinuance (Ripple, Alexander, and Polemis, 1964, p. 117). Clients who returned for a fifth interview were defined as "continuers." We have summarized the findings of the two studies in Table 1.3. Notice that the original five categories were collapsed into three: High, Moderate, and Low.[2]

As you can see, the higher the rating for hope, the higher the likelihood the client continued past the fourth interview. This kind of accumulated evidence will validate the scale's ability to predict. Such criteria will help substantiate the assumption of interval-level data, as, over time, the scale items take on real meaning.

---

[2]In the years before easy access to computers, it was common practice to simplify data by collapsing it into nominal or, as in this case, ordinal categories and then calculate chi-squares by hand. The result was a great reduction in the power of the analysis.

The degree to which the client appears hopeful that his problem can be resolved, not necessarily by or with the agency.

Very High	1
High	2
Moderate	3
Low	4
Very Low	5

FIGURE 1.10 Question with Sample Response Scale

The second method for supporting ordinal-level data as interval-level data entails comparing the results of non-parametric statistical tests with parametric tests. The more powerful parametric tests require interval-level data. If ordinal-level data is run with both types and the results are similar, then no harm is done in making the assumption that the data is suitable for parametric analysis.

Over the years, wonderful work has been done in the development of nonparametric tests. One could argue that parametric tests are not needed for *bivariate analysis* (that is, a comparison of the relationship between two variables or characteristics), even though such tests may be more familiar. However, it's a multivariate world, and for multivariate analysis we need interval-level data.

Our example of this second procedure is taken from the development of an instrument that measures psychoso-

TABLE 1.3 Levels of Measurement: A Summary

Level of Measurement	Variable		Ordered	Statistical Tests	
	Discrete	Continuous		Nonparametric	Parametric
Nominal	Yes	No	No	Yes	No
Ordinal	Yes	No	Yes	Yes	No
Interval	No	Yes	Yes	No	Yes
Ratio	No	Yes	Yes	No	Yes

Child Behavior Problems

Emotional or behavioral problems of the child can include, but are not limited to, running away, aggression, withdrawal, truancy, psychosexual disturbances, stealing, and abuse of alcohol or drugs.

Question 1. How serious do you consider the child's problems are regarding his or her behavior?

1. Not at all serious (problems not discernible)
2. Somewhat serious (problems observable, but solvable *without* outside help)
3. Moderately serious (ability to solve problems is questionable without outside help)
4. Serious (problems impede normal child functioning and are not solvable without outside help)
5. Very serious (problems indicate dissolution of family unit if allowed to continue)

FIGURE 1.11 Degree-of-Seriousness Scale with Sample Question

cial assessment in clinical child welfare (Curtis, Rosman, and Pappenfort, 1984). The instrument contains 16 questions, 2 in each of eight areas of psychosocial assessment. One of the 2 questions asks the respondent to assess the degree of seriousness of problems in that area. The other question asks the respondent to evaluate assets and resources. Figure 1.11 contains a sample question and the "degree-of-seriousness" scale.

The scale contains five ordered responses that the authors attempted to define. For instance, in Figure 1.11, response 5, Very Serious, was defined as "problems indicate dissolution of family unit if allowed to continue."

With a total of 16 questions, the authors were able to obtain 16 variables for analysis. Using a nonparametric statistical test, every item was crosstabulated with every other item. The result was 120 tables (16×16 minus the 136 tables that were duplicated or resulted from an item

TABLE 1.4 Enhancing the Power of Statistical Data Analysis

Area	Weakest	Strongest
Means of Data Analysis	Manual	Computer
Sample Size	Small	At least 30
Sampling Method	Non-random	Random
Levels of Measurement	Nominal	Ratio

being compared with itself). Of the 120 possible relationships, 87 were *significant,* meaning that the demonstrated relationships did not appear to result from chance.

The same procedure was run using a comparable parametric test. Of the 120 possible relationships, 86 were significant. Of all the relationships, only three were different from those derived from the nonparametric test. The three mismatched relationships were minutely different.

The authors concluded that the use of parametric tests in the second instance did not distort, but confirmed the results obtained with the nonparametric. This was good evidence that the ordered categories in the "degree-of-seriousness" scale did, in fact, represent real differences and, therefore, real rather than arbitrary numbers.

1.5 Summary

Table 1.4 summarizes what we have said in this chapter about computers, sample size, sampling method, and levels of measurement.

We have tried to convince you how limited a data analysis is without a computer. But we have also offered suggestions about how best to conduct an analysis by hand, when that is necessary. In terms of sample size, more is better. We have tried to convince you of the advantages of random sampling and warn you away from the use of nonrandom methods, such as choosing study subjects for the sake of convenience. We reviewed levels of measurement, maybe for the umpteenth time for you, for the sake of encouraging you to plan for and seek out interval and ratio level data.

In this chapter we have tried to orient you to planning in a manner that will help you get the most out of numbers. We have one more chapter with hints and helpful starters before we arrive at what to do when the numbers are in.

CHAPTER 2

Getting the Most Out of Numbers: Some Starters

Analysis begins before you collect any data. We said that before and it's worth repeating. What follows are a few techniques that will help you store and use your data easily and efficiently. Even though many of our ideas and suggestions are the kinds of things an experienced researcher might do intuitively, we think it is useful to present step-by-step, systematic procedures that will aid you in getting the most information possible from your data.

We are making the assumption that you have collected the data yourself, and that you did not obtain it from someone else or from the U.S. Census Bureau. If you did, not all of our comments about the planning and cleaning phases of data analysis will be applicable.

2.1 Computer Programs for Social Science Statistics

There are several complete statistical packages available for social science data analysis, as well as a number of excellent single-purpose programs in specific techniques. We have chosen two computer programs for our examples in this book, however, that offer a good range of techniques: the Statistical Analysis System (SAS) and the Statistical Package for the Social Sciences (SPSS-X). These two are sufficiently different to offer a contrast, and one or both are likely to be available in your area.

Each of them has a basic structure, or grammar, with which you need to become familiar. For example, SAS ends command statements with a semicolon, and SPSS-X ends command statements with a slash. To the computer, they both mean "Stop, the next words are a different sentence." There are other distinctions in the way you use the programs, but they are only important to the computer, not to you, as long as you copy them exactly.

The introductory guides to the statistical packages, such as SPSS-X, or SAS, do a good job of explaining how to code and store data by computer should you need an orientation to those skills. Obviously, they are also guides to writing the programs that process the data. The commands that you will need to run those programs are system dependent so you will have to consult with your local computer center. If you are using a microcomputer, you may have to wade through the owner's manual on your own.

There are several things you should keep in mind when dealing with a computer center. Often they are oriented to those individuals in business and the sciences using powerful number-crunching programming languages like FORTRAN, PL/I, or COBOL. The available "user-friendly live ware" or consultants may not be that friendly or patient or simply may not be familiar with the statistical packages most often used in the social sciences. Another problem is documentation, the instructions one needs to use a system. Computer centers are notorious for incomprehensible documentation or very little documentation at all. Do not ask consultants at a computer center questions such as "How do I write an SPSS-X program?" You will find they are unavailable and unmotivated to help. First, try to educate yourself enough to ask questions such as, "I tried this, but it didn't work and the computer gave me an error message. What went wrong?"

Your best bet is to learn from someone who has been through it before. Consider taking a course in statistics that includes the use of computerized statistical packages. Beware, however, of highly technical courses in data processing because they will only sidetrack you from your purpose.

2.2 Assigning Case Numbers

All your data should have one common denominator. It will be grouped according to some case or observation.[1] Examples may include people, states of the union, or points in time such as days or years. It is, therefore, important to create a variable, e.g., called CASE, that will be common to every case or observation. Statistical packages assign numbers to each observation in the output. However, computer output will not help you find a problem case in a stack of 500 questionnaires on your desk. For that you may need a bright red case number on every questionnaire that corresponds to a variable CASE on the data set. The need for this will become more apparent when we discuss cleaning the data.

2.3 Storing the Data

In the conduct of any research, you have to collect data, store it, and find it again. How you store it so you can find it again should be an important part of your planning. If you mail out a questionnaire, gather those that are returned, and code them and key them for the computer, storing the data may not be a problem. You may be able to include the *job control language* (JCL is the system-dependent instructions necessary for processing), the program, and the data on one computer file or data set. You

---

[1]Sometimes one needs file structures that are hierarchical, i.e., that contain more than one common denominator. See the SPSS-X or SAS manuals for an explanation.

TABLE 2.1 Sample Instrument-Numbering Scheme

	Time 1	Time 2	Time 3
Instrument	#1A	#1B	#1C
Instrument	#2A	#2B	#2C

can then process the data by running what are often termed express jobs.

But suppose you have multiple instruments and multiple data collection points? In order to maintain the common denominator—the unique case or observation—data are usually stored on separate data sets. We have devised the following system for doing that. Number the instruments sequentially; for example, if there are six instruments, number them Instrument #1A to Instrument #6A. If Instrument #1A is administered again to the same subjects, call it Instrument #1B at Time 2, #1C at Time 3, and so on, as shown in Table 2.1.

Now store that data physically in that order and, by naming the files or data sets correctly, *store that data on the computer in the exact same order.*

Store the data from Instrument #1A into a computer file or data set called FILE1A.DATA. DATA is a standard designation for a raw data *input file.* Store the JCL and the program for that data into a file called FILE1A.CNTL. CNTL is a standard designation for a *control file.* If needed, when the job is run the system will create what is called a *saved file,* a file that contains the data formatted for analysis. Saved files should also end up in some standardized manner, depending on what package or computer system you are using to process the data. If you ask the computer to list your files, it will list them in the order you have stored them, both physically and by computer. Figure 2.1 shows an example of such a computer list.

CATALOG

FILE1A.CNTL
FILE1A.DATA
FILE1A.SAVE
FILE2A.CNTL
FILE2A.DATA
FILE2A.SAVE

FIGURE 2.1 Example of Computer File List

2.4 Cleaning the Data

At this point we are going to assume that you have collected your data, coded it, keyed it for computer storage, and are ready to begin your analysis. When we talk about cleaning data, we mean accounting for the data. We want to eliminate as much data as we can that appears in error or ends up missing. Obviously, data coded in error will distort the meaning of an analysis and missing data will reduce the power of an analysis. For example, if you want to know the average age of your sample, but several individuals appear to be 1,500 years old, you have a problem. Missing data can also be a serious problem when you want to run a statistical procedure using multiple variables, because often when the procedure detects one piece of missing data, the entire case or observation will be deleted from the analysis. And the less data, the less there will be to say about your project.

In order to differentiate each possibility, we suggest the scheme shown in Figure 2.2 or your own variation thereof.

In the case of telephone or face-to-face interviews, you may want to have a missing code for responses that are refused.

These differences in missing and unavailable data may not seem important and, in some circumstances, they may not be. But the point is that trying to account for missing

Response	Code
Correct	Exact value, e.g., 075
Missing	999
Error	888
Does Not Apply	777

FIGURE 2.2 Sample Answer Codes

data after it's on the computer and coded with only one missing code can be very confusing.

Another source of confusion can be the failure to distinguish between missing data and data with an assigned value of zero. Consider the questions in Figure 2.3. We need the three columns, 6–8, in order to code whether or not each response was circled. If there was contact with the father, we would code 1 if the response was circled, 0 if not.

Columns

Question 3. Did you have any contact with your father in the past year?
(Please circle one response only.)

/5

No _____ 0
Yes _____ 1

Question 4. If you did have contact with your father, what kinds of things did you do together?
(Please circle all responses that apply.)

/6–8

Spoke on the telephone _____ 1
Visited together _____ 2
Other _____ 3

FIGURE 2.3 Sample Questions for Missing Versus Zero Codes

Columns

Question 1. Is your father living?
(Please circle one response only.)

/1

No _____ 0
Yes _____ 1

Question 2. If your father is alive, how old is he?
(Please fill in the blank.)

_____   /2–4

FIGURE 2.4 Sample Questions and Missing Data

In this case, 0 means they did *not* speak on the telephone or otherwise. Zero means negation or the absence of something. If there was no contact indicated in Question 3 and the responses in Question 4 were appropriately skipped, we would code 7 for each item, meaning *does not apply.*

2.4.1 Assigning Missing Values

When we get to the point of looking at a frequency distribution and beginning to clean the data, we want to account for it, all of it. It is therefore necessary to plan how to treat the data that, for one reason or another, will not be available. Depending on the purpose and the circumstances, it may be necessary to distinguish among data that was missing for no apparent reason, that was refused, that was given erroneously, and that did not apply.

For example, consider the possible reasons for missing answers to Question 2 in Figure 2.4. Note the column numbers on the right. We left one column in order to code either a 0 for No or a 1 for Yes. In the second question we allowed three columns for the father's age (because the father could be 100 years old or older). Suppose the father is alive and he is 75 years old. For columns 1–4 we code 1075.

	Question 2	
Question 1	**Answered**	**Blank**
Father Alive	Correct	Missing
Father Not Alive	Error	Correct/Does Not Apply

FIGURE 2.5 Possible Missing-Data Outcomes

Simple. Suppose the father is not alive and Question 2 is blank. The response to Question 2 is blank because it *does not apply.* On the other hand, suppose the father is alive and Question 2 is blank. The data is *missing,* probably passed over or refused by the respondent. Finally, suppose the father is not alive, but his age is given as 75. The data looks as if it were provided *in error.* These possibilities are summed up in Figure 2.5.

2.4.2 Using a Frequency Distribution

A useful procedure for cleaning data is to run a frequency distribution. Whether you use SAS, SPSS-X, some other statistical package, or do the procedure by hand, it should look something like the example in Table 2.2.

The variable name, SEX, is followed by the variable title or label, Sex of the Respondent. There are two values to this variable, Male and Female. Depending on what statistical package you use and in what form you stored the variable,

TABLE 2.2 Sample Frequency Distribution

SEX	Sex of the Respondent		
	Absolute Frequency	*Percent Frequency*	*Cumulative Frequency (%)*
Male	16	38.1	38.1
Female	26	61.9	100.0
Total	42	100.0	

a value number such as 0 for Male and 1 for Female may be printed next to the words Male and Female. Subsequent columns tell you how many males and females there are in the distribution, which is referred to as the *absolute frequency,* as well as in the *percent frequency,* that is, what percent of the total distribution each value contributes. The final column gives you the *cumulative frequency* by percent, that is, the percentage of the total distribution contributed by each value up to and including that value. Percentages are rounded to one decimal point.

Table 2.3 contains a *frequency distribution* with numerous problems.

This frequency distribution contains value labels with value codes next to them. The value 0 has no label. This could be an error. Possibly the coder used a 0 when Missing (9) was intended. On the other hand, the value 0 and the absolute frequency 2 may be correct. Maybe there is supposed to be a category of None for no religion and the value label is missing.

One respondent was coded as a 6. That value probably should not exist. That may also be the problem with the 8 unless 8 means Refused, an alternate missing code, in which case the value label is missing again.

Before we discuss how to go about identifying the problem cases, we want to present one more complication. See Table 2.4.

After we attempted to identify our respondents by religion, we wanted to know whether or not the Catholics lived in Chicago. We knew there were at least 17 Catholics from Table 2.3, but in Table 2.4 there are only 15 Catholics identified by residence. Moreover, the number of non-Catholics in Table 2.4 who were supposed to skip the item does not equal the number of non-Catholics originally identified.

Let's go back to Table 2.3 and assume 0 meant None and that 6 and 8 were really Missing. That means there were actually 17 respondents identified as Catholic. Although

TABLE 2.3 Sample Frequency Distribution with Errors

RELIGION		Religion of the Respondent		
		Absolute Frequency	Percent Frequency	Cumulative Frequency (%)
	0.	2	4.2	4.2
Catholic	1.	17	35.4	39.6
Jewish	2.	14	29.2	68.8
Protestant	3.	9	18.7	87.5
Other	4.	1	2.1	89.6
	6.	1	2.1	91.7
	8.	1	2.1	93.8
Missing	9.	3	6.2	100.0
Total		48	100.0	

we do not know which respondent was which, we can guess, by deduction, that (1) one of the missing cases in Table 2.4 is a Catholic whose data regarding residence is missing and (2) one of the Not Catholic cases *is* Catholic, but data regarding residence is also missing.

However, we do not want to guess. We want to make sure and also identify which cases contain the problem codes. That means we have to go back to the original data collection instruments. To do that we need to identity the problem cases.

TABLE 2.4 Sample Frequency Distribution with Further Errors

CATHOLIC	Residence of Catholic Respondents		
	Absolute Frequency	Percent Frequency	Cumulative Frequency (%)
Not Catholic	27	56.3	56.3
Chicago	9	18.7	75.0
Other City	6	12.5	87.5
Missing	6	12.5	100.0
Total	48	100.0	

There are essentially three methods of identifying which cases contain coding errors. The first involves searching by hand: if there are not too many cases, this may be the simplest and easiest method. The second method consists of listing by computer the values of all the variables that contain errors. Don't forget the case number variable. The procedures are PROC PRINT in SAS, LIST CASES in SPSS Version 9, and PRINT in SPSS-X.

If you have too many cases for this method, you may want to identify the problem observations by using conditional statements that define the errors and then print the case numbers as frequencies using PROC FREQ in SAS or FREQUENCIES in SPSS-X. For example, refer back to Tables 2.3 and 2.4. If you write a conditional statement in your program that selects those cases in which the variable RELIGION has a value of Catholic and the variable CATHOLIC does *not* have a value of Chicago or Other City, then printing the variable for case number using PROC FREQ or FREQUENCIES should result in identifying those two cases that are Catholic but where the residence is missing. Checking the original data collection instrument will tell you if the information is retrievable or not.

If you have retrievable data, there are two things you can do to correct the problems. Again, choosing which method is better depends on your judgment as to which one is more economical. First, you can go back and edit your raw data computer file. The attempt to find the correct lines and columns to change can cause headaches, but it may be necessary if your errors are idiosyncratic. If there appears to be some pattern to your errors, however, an alternative method may help. This involves using recode statements in your program. For example, if the 0's in Table 2.3 actually reflect missing data, you can insert a statement in your program that, for the variable RELIGION, the value 0 equals the missing value 9.

CHAPTER 3

Describing the Data

The purpose of this chapter is two-fold: (1) to show how data is organized and described, whether for display or for your own scrutiny, and (2) to discuss the use of descriptive statistics. At the end of this chapter, we will also demonstrate how to present a well-constructed table.

3.1 Data Organization and Description

We wish we could show you the one best way of organizing and describing data, but how data is presented depends on how it was collected, that is, the levels of measurement, how much data there is, and what your purpose is.

There are four basic methods of describing data: in a narrative, in a frequency distribution, in a crosstabulation, and graphically. These four methods are summarized in Figure 3.1. We will show you an example of each method and discuss its pros and cons. We will use as an example data regarding the sex, age, and race of ten children attending a therapeutic school. The raw data are found in Table 3.1.

3.1.1 Narrative Description

All the data about the ten children in our sample is found in the narrative description below. The narrative is com-

I. Narration
II. Frequency Distribution
    A. Ungrouped Data
    B. Grouped Data
III. Crosstabulation
    A. Two Variables
    B. Three or More
       Variables
IV. Graphic Display
    A. Bar Chart
    B. Histogram
    C. Pie Chart

FIGURE 3.1: Methods of Data Description

plete and, as far as the data will allow, in depth. However, an overview of the sample is buried in the text.

There are ten children attending a therapeutic school program. Six are female and four are male. Two children are 6 years old, one is 7, two are 8 years old, and one each is 9, 11, 12, 13, and 16 years old. Seven are black, two white, and one is of Asian descent.

TABLE 3.1 Sex, Age, and Race of Ten Therapeutic-School Students

Case 1	Female	6	Black
Case 2	Male	6	Asian
Case 3	Male	7	Black
Case 4	Female	8	Black
Case 5	Female	9	Black
Case 6	Female	8	White
Case 7	Male	11	Black
Case 8	Female	16	Black
Case 9	Female	13	White
Case 10	Male	12	Black

TABLE 3.2 Frequency Distribution of Ten Therapeutic-School Students—Ungrouped Data

Age	f
6	2
7	1
8	2
9	1
11	1
12	1
13	1
16	1
Total	10

3.1.2 Frequency Distribution

A *frequency distribution* is a simple method of summarizing data in a table. An example of a frequency distribution containing the ages of the ten children is found in Table 3.2.

If there is a large number of cases and/or a wide range of ages, one might want to group the data as in Table 3.3. Remember to maintain equal class intervals when dealing with interval- and ratio-level data.

TABLE 3.3 Frequency Distribution of Ten Therapeutic-School Students—Grouped Data

Age	f
6–7	3
8–9	3
10–11	1
12–13	2
14–15	0
16–17	1
Total	10

TABLE 3.4 Therapeutic-School Students by Sex and Race

	Race		
Sex	*Black*	*White*	*Asian*
Male	3	0	1
Female	4	2	0

The frequency distribution is a simple, clear method of organizing data. Because the display is limited to one variable, however, it may not be suitable for presentation in a final report.

The usefulness of these techniques will vary with circumstances. A simple frequency distribution of the children's ages may only be a device for your own understanding and preliminary to further analysis. On the other hand, if you are applying for a grant, one of whose criteria is that you provide services to children between the ages of 6 and 16, the data takes on special meaning, crosses an invisible line and becomes information, that is, usable knowledge.

3.1.3 Crosstabulation

The use of *crosstabulations* allows the display of two or more variables at once and, thereby, the identification of subgroups in the sample by key variables. Crosstabulations are usually reserved for nominal-level data and, as will be seen in a later chapter, can be analyzed statistically. Table 3.4 is a crosstabulation of the two nominal-level variables Race and Sex.

We already know that most of the children are black, but revealed in Table 3.4 is the fact that being black is not related to the sex of the child. There are almost an equal number of black males and females. There are no white males. All of this is, of course, out of context. We do not

TABLE 3.5 Sex and Age of Therapeutic-School Students by Race

Sex	Race		
	Black	White	Asian
Male	3	0	1
Female	4	2	0
Age			
6–7	2	0	1
8–9	2	1	0
10–11	1	0	0
12–13	1	1	0
14–15	0	0	0
16–17	1	0	0

know what the data mean, if anything. We do not know how the children came to attend the school, what their problems are or whether the location of the school contributes to the racial composition of the students, but this simple crosstabulation raises some important questions. It helps us identify both what we know and do not know. If the study was planned carefully, the questions can be answered with data regarding additional variables.

It is also possible to construct a crosstabulation containing more than two variables, as seen in Table 3.5, where sex and age are broken down by race. No relationship between age and race is revealed in Table 3.5. Except for idiographic statements such as "one of the youngest children is Asian" and "the oldest child is black," we cannot say, for example, that the black children represent a certain age group. If we want to crosstabulate sex with age, it is better to begin another table.

The crosstabulation can be a simple but revealing device for describing data. However, we caution against reporting too many variables at once and constructing tables that are too complicated. Some researchers like to summarize all their descriptive findings on one large table and you may want to do that too, but try to refrain from running a table from one page to the next.

3.1.4 Graphic Displays

Using graphs and other visual aids is probably the best way to communicate the meaning of data as long as what you want to communicate is not too complicated. They can be clear, eye-catching, and can even help alleviate some of the distortion of data caused by descriptive statistics. (More about that in the second half of this chapter.)

The most common forms of graphic display are the bar chart, the histogram, and the pie chart. Figure 3.2 contains data regarding the race of the children from our therapeutic school in a *bar chart*.

The advantage of such a visual display is evident: one can see immediately that the great majority of the students are black children.

Histograms are similar to bar charts. However, the visual representation of the frequency is vertical rather than horizontal. See Figure 3.3. In this example, as in the bar chart, the proportions of racial distribution are evident.

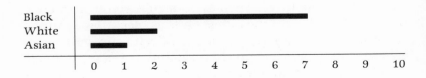

FIGURE 3.2 Races of Therapeutic-School Students: Bar Chart

```
10
 9
 8
 7        *
 6        *
 5        *
 4        *
 3        *
 2        *          *
 1        *          *          *

       Black      White      Asian
```

FIGURE 3.3   Races of Therapeutic-School Students: Histogram

Histograms also allow one to look closely at the nature of the distribution, for example, whether the distribution approximates the normal curve. In fact, in SPSS-X one can request a normal curve to be superimposed upon the histogram for comparison.

Pie charts are circles divided proportionately by percentage of the distribution as seen in Figure 3.4. It is another useful way of displaying data in a visually appealing manner.

Another important method of visual display is the scatter plot, but we will save that for the chapters on bivariate relationships and multiple regression analysis. More advanced researchers may want to look into the use of visual techniques found in the area of exploratory data analysis (Tukey, 1977; Hartwig and Dearing, 1979).

3.2 Descriptive Statistics

By *descriptive statistics,* we mean statistics that summarize data either by measuring central tendency or variability. *Measurements of central tendency* attempt to describe a sample in the simplest, most understandable man-

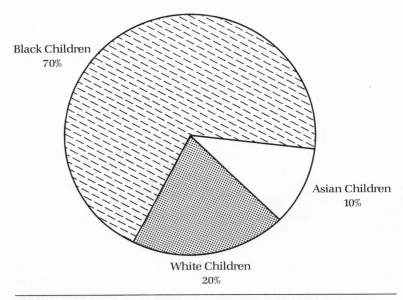

FIGURE 3.4 Races of Therapeutic-School Students: Pie Chart

ner. The most common measures are the mean, median and mode, all used to describe the average or typical respondent, case, or observation.

Measurements of variability or dispersion are used to describe the degree to which the individuals within a distribution deviate from the aforementioned average or typical respondent, case, or observation. *Variability* refers to the spread of a distribution. Common measures include the minimum value, the maximum value, the range, the standard deviation, and the variance. Figure 3.5 contains a summary list of the most common descriptive statistics.

Before we explain these statistics and how they are used, be warned that descriptive statistics must be chosen and used judiciously, depending on the nature of your data and your purpose. The goal is to enhance your data analysis, communicate your findings, and avoid distor-

I. Measures of Central Tendency
   A. Mean
   B. Median
   C. Mode
II. Measures of Dispersion
   A. Minimum Value
   B. Maximum Value
   C. Range
   D. Standard Deviation
   E. Variance

FIGURE 3.5 Summary List of Descriptive Statistics

tion. Each descriptive statistic has its uses and its advantages as well as its potential to distort.

3.2.1 The Mean

The *statistical mean* is a simple arithmetic average: it is the sum of the values for each case or observation divided by the total number of cases. In the example of our hypothetical school, if we sum the ages of all the students and divide by ten students, the resulting mean is 9.6 years. The average or typical student is just a little over $9\frac{1}{2}$ years old.

You can also express the mean as a percentage. If you schedule 20 appointments with a client and he misses three, then the client has an attendance average of 85% (17 appointments divided by 20 equals .85 or 85% of the total).

The mean is often designated by the symbol X. The other descriptive statistics have symbols or abbreviations too, but to avoid confusion, we prefer to spell the words out.

3.2.2 The Median

The *median,* sometimes abbreviated as Md, is the middle point in the distribution; half the observations fall below it and half fall above it. In other words, it is the 50th percentile. If we had 11 students in our therapeutic school, the median age would be the age of the sixth child, the one in the middle, counting from either end. Because we have ten students in our example, we split the difference between the fifth student, age 8, and the sixth, age 9, and, by convention, call the median 8.5 years.

For a moment, refer back to Table 3.3 and notice that, when the data is grouped, we cannot be sure where exactly within the category 8–9 the median lies. For that problem there is a relatively simple formula we can use:

$$Md = L + W \left[\frac{(N/2) - CF}{f} \right]$$

L is the lowest value in the group that contains the 50th percentile, W is the width or class interval of the category containing the median, N is the total number of observations, CF is the cumulative frequency, that is, the number of cases up to, but not including the category that contains the median, and f is the frequency or number of cases in the category containing the median. Essentially, the formula takes into account the nature of the category that contains the median and the relative strengths of the categories around it.

$$Md = 8 + 2 \left[\frac{(10/2 - 3)}{3} \right]$$

$$Md = 9.33$$

If we plug our data from the therapeutic school into the formula, the resulting median is 9.33 years. By the simpler method, and in this case, the preferred one, the median is 8.5 years. This discrepancy is caused by (1) an imperfect world and (2) the small size of the sample.

Level of Measurement	Measure of Central Tendency
Nominal	Mode
Ordinal	Mode, Median
Interval/Ratio	Mode, Median, Mean

FIGURE 3.6 Level of Measurement and Central Tendency

3.2.3 The Mode

The *mode,* sometimes abbreviated as Mo, is the value or category with the greatest number of cases or observations. Some distributions are *bimodal,* meaning there are two values and two groups with the greatest number of cases.

Like the mean and median, the mode should not be confused with frequencies. In Table 3.2, the modes are six years old and eight years old, for example, not 3 and 3.

3.2.4 Central Tendency and Levels of Measurement

The appropriate use of the mean, median, and mode largely depends on the data's level of measurement; these uses are summarized in Figure 3.6. With interval/ratio-level data like age and income, you can use them all. With nominal and ordinal level data, there are limitations. With nominal, categorical data, only the mode can be used. Realistically, it might be more revealing to refer to the category with the largest percentage of cases rather than the mode. When ordinal-level data is available, it is possible to use both the mode and the median. The median can also be used with ordinal grouped data, even when the class intervals are uneven.

3.2.5 Relationship Between Mean, Median, and Mode

We are certain that all of you have seen a diagram of the normal distribution, a kind of two-dimensional flying saucer. When a frequency distribution is normal, the mean, median, and mode are equal and represent the value with the largest frequency.

Unless you take random samples of large numbers, however, the mean, median, and mode are rarely the same. When they are not equal, each can tell you something different about your subjects. That is why using only one descriptive statistic can distort your findings. It is better to report how each one relates to the others.

A good example of comparing the mean and median is found in Gideon Horowitz's *Sadistic Statistics* (1981). He describes a hypothetical group of workers earning an annual income with a mean of $12,375 and a median of $7,000. During contract negotiations between labor and management, each side emphasizes only the mean or median to their advantage.

The discrepancy between mean and median is commonplace and should always be considered. Because the mean is sensitive to extreme cases, very high or very low values will pull the mean away from the median or 50th percentile. In the above example, a few atypical workers with salaries substantially over $12,000 are pulling up the mean. Management takes advantage of this because it looks like their workers are better off as a group than they are.

The same thing happens with the data from our hypothetical school. The mean is 9.6 years, the median 8.5 years. The two oldest children, the 13-year-old and the 16-year-old, pull up the mean. If the two oldest children are taken out of the calculations, the median drops 0.5 years to 8 years, while the mean drops a full 1.2 years to 8.4 years.

If all the numbers are presented at once, a mean of 9.6

years, a median of 8.5 years, and modes of 6 and 8 years, we can communicate clearly the finding that the program primarily serves latency-age children.

3.2.6 The Range

Although the program primarily serves latency-age children, there are two teenagers in the school. Using only the mean, median, and mode to describe the program fully is not enough. We need to report measurements of variability, in this case the range.

The *range* is simply the distance from the minimum value to the maximum value, in this case, from 6 years to 16 years, for a range of 10 years. This simple descriptive measure of variability can tell us a lot about our subjects. Although the therapeutic school serves primarily latency-age children, quite a few resources in space, supplies, staff training, and staff experience would be needed to run a program that serves both 6- and 16-year-olds. The greater the range, the greater the variation in needs.

3.2.7 The Standard Deviation

It is possible that any given group of human subjects will be heterogeneous or, on any given characteristic, will vary greatly. The most common statistical measure of this variability is called the *standard deviation*. It is simply a measure of the extent by which individual frequencies deviate from the mean. Among the children in our therapeutic school, the standard deviation should be relatively large. If everyone were the same age, the standard deviation would be zero because there would be no variability from the average age. (The mean, median, and mode would be the same.)

The formula for the standard deviation, usually abbreviated as *s,* is as follows:

$$ s = \sqrt{\frac{\Sigma \times^2}{N}} $$

or the square root of the sum (Σ) of all the deviations from the mean squared (X^2) and then divided by the sample size (N). If you are unfortunate enough not to have access to a computer and must calculate this statistic by hand, consult any elementary statistics book for more detailed step-by-step procedures.

The standard deviation for age in our therapeutic school is 3.14 years. The number 3.14 is a measure of standard deviation units, plus or minus, from the mean. If the standard deviation were larger, the variability within the group would be greater, and if it were smaller, the variability would be smaller. Because one standard deviation unit from the mean, plus or minus, constitutes about one-third of all the cases, a standard deviation of 3.14 years means that approximately two-thirds of all the children range in age from about 6.5 years (the mean 9.6 minus 3.14) to 12.7 years (the mean 9.6 plus 3.14).

As we guessed, a standard deviation of 3.14 years for 10 children with a mean of 9.6 years is quite large and indicates a rather flat, spread-out distribution. That is easy to see just from our raw data, but if there were hundreds of cases, such a standard deviation would be a helpful summary statistic in describing such a spread in age.

One more thing before we proceed. The standard deviation, like the mean, is very sensitive to extreme values. This is true of the calculation of any statistic where the values are squared at some point in the procedure. If the 16-year-old is dropped from our calculations, the standard deviation drops from 3.14 to 2.53 years. If one of the 6-year-old children is excluded, the standard deviation drops only to 3.08 years.

3.2.8 The Variance

If the standard deviation is squared, the resulting statistic is called the *variance*. In the case of our therapeutic school, it is 9.84 years. The variance is not an interpretable statistic, but it is very useful in the calculation of more advanced statistics, as you will see in upcoming chapters.

3.2.9 Elements of a Good Table

Someone once told us he never read the articles in a journal, only the tables. He may not be unusual. Therefore, it is a good idea to (1) present your tables in an understandable format and (2) use tables to summarize all your major findings.

If you have a college degree and you cannot understand a table, it is probably not your fault. Here is a list of do's and don't's for tables—and many of them are often disregarded.

1. Don't make a table too complicated. It should be obvious without a narrative.
2. The title should describe all the data in the table.
3. Don't present nonsignificant findings unless they are *very important.*
4. The first table in a report should include information regarding the *entire sample.* Subsequent tables that report data on subsamples should indicate why the *N* is different.
5. When reporting statistics, present all necessary information including the statistic, its value, the degrees of freedom, and the confidence level. Example: chi-square = 3.85, DF = 3, P < .01. (We will review these terms in the next chapter.)
6. Try not to use obscure abbreviations.
7. Percentages are usually totaled vertically.

TABLE 3.6 Ages of Ten Children at a Therapeutic School

Age of Children	Number	Percent
6–10	6	60%
11–15	3	30
16–20	1	10
Total	10	100%

8. As a general rule, when using grouped data, make the class intervals in units of 5.

See Table 3.6 for a sample table.

The usefulness of data collection and analysis ultimately depends on communication and comparability. How well you communicate your results through graphic displays, tables, and descriptive statistics determines their value to others. The value of your results also depends on how comparable and relevant they are to another group of human subjects.

You may have spent two years working with a group of unmarried mothers. How well you describe those young women allows other human-service workers to decide how helpful your experiences will be to them. If you work with 16-year-olds in a high-school program, your conclusions may be of little use to someone who is working with 25-year-old AFDC mothers. However, your findings may be of great interest to another high-school-based worker. Your thoughtful use of descriptive techniques will help in making that judgment.

CHAPTER 4

Relationships Between Two Characteristics

This chapter is about taking two to tango: linking two characteristics and testing for a relationship. The number of statistics that measure *bivariate relationships* are staggering and continue to proliferate, but essentially, they all do only one of three things:

1. They crosstabulate categorical data.
2. They compare averages or compare the central tendencies between two sample groups or between a sample and its population.
3. They correlate ordinal or interval-level characteristics.

All these concepts will be discussed in detail along with examples of the most commonly used statistical tests. The chapter will conclude by placing the utility of bivariate tests into an overall data-analysis framework.

From this point on, we will not present any more statistical formulas in the text (except to explain a concept) or any more hands-and-toes calculations. They are simply not realistic. Some statistics, like the chi-square for a 2×2 crosstabulation, are relatively easy to calculate by hand, but a typical data analysis can entail running on the computer more than 100 chi-square tests for exploratory purposes.

4.1 Vocabulary

Before we go on to explain the tests themselves, we need to review some basic vocabulary. The sections will be clearly labeled so you can skip what you do not need to review. As we have tried to do all along, we will forsake technical definitions for functional, applied definitions. A second word of caution related to our purpose: our definitions may not be exactly the same as other authors'. But only God writes in stone; scientists use word processors. What we provide here is what we have found useful.

4.1.1 Validity

Validity is a concept from measurement theory having to do with the truthfulness of measurement. You have probably heard that validity means measuring what you intend to measure. Technically speaking, that is a good definition of *internal validity. External validity* refers to the extent to which a measurement can be generalized; for example, the extent to which data describing a sample can be inferred to represent a larger group of people from which the data were drawn.

4.1.2 Relationships

Relationship is a generic term meaning a linkage or coexistence. The word does not imply cause and effect, strength, or direction. For example, if men tend to be more interested in sports than women, then gender is related to interest in sports. If the more that people want help, the more likely they are to benefit from psychotherapy, then success in psychotherapy is related to motivation.

Under the general rubric of *relationship,* there are three additional terms with rather specific meanings.

Association. An *association* is a kind of relationship in which an assumption of cause and effect is specifically avoided. The word is generally used to describe linkages between categories. For example, if Protestants tend to be Republicans, then religion is associated with political affiliation. Notice the implication that Protestantism and Republicanism coexist, but it may be something else that is causing the linkage between the two variables.

Difference. *Difference* means the state of being not equal. In research terms, the importance lies in what is not equal, in this case, averages or central tendency. The implication is that the characteristic being compared can be counted at the ordinal or interval level. For example, if people who move to the Sunbelt are older than people who stay in the Midwest, then the two groups are different in age. Notice that we can just as easily say that age is related to moving to the Sunbelt, but the word *different* specifically refers to nonequivalency in average age.

Correlation. A *correlation* is a kind of relationship in which the characteristics fluctuate by direction. There are positive correlations and negative correlations. In a positive correlation, high values in one characteristic correspond to high values in another, or low values in one characteristic correspond to low values in another. In a negative correlation, high values in one characteristic correspond to low values in another. Positive and negative refer to direction only and are not relevant to the strength of the relationship. For example, if the more time and money an agency spends on recruitment, the more foster parents it finds, then effort positively correlates with the number of foster parents recruited. If the older the client, the more he or she benefits from insight-oriented psychotherapy, then age positively correlates with insight. If the more service that people receive, the fewer social problems they have, then service delivery negatively correlates with problems. With correlation, direction is everything and you have to watch it carefully. For example, service delivery would positively correlate with *reduction* in problems: the more service, the more reduction in problems.

4.1.3 Cause and Prediction

A *causal relationship* is one in which one characteristic has a direct effect on another. Some authors argue that there are no causal relationships that can be substantiated with statistics due to the absence of laboratory controls on the subjects. However, it is common to use the terms *independent* and *dependent variables*—which imply cause and effect—when it is logical to do so. We tend to accept the common practice.

A *predictive relationship* is one in which one characteristic has a measurable effect on another. For example, suppose we find that women tend to benefit from psychotherapy more than men do. If we assume that nothing else is intervening in the relationship, we could describe the relationship in causal terms and say that gender causes success because being born male or female pre-dates participation in psychotherapy (obviously, we can't say that success causes gender). However, if the relationship is thought of in terms of prediction, two problems are eliminated. First, cause and effect does not have to be assumed. Gender predicts the presence of success regardless of whatever causes success. Second, prediction can go in either direction. Thus, it can also be concluded that among a group of successful psychotherapy patients, most of them will be women.

4.1.4 Hypothesis

A *hypothesis* is a proposition linking two or more characteristics. All the examples used in the previous sections are implied hypotheses. For example, service delivery is related to reduction in social problems, or gender is related to success in psychotherapy. Such statements are commonly referred to as *alternative hypotheses. Null hypotheses* (often written as H_o) are the negative or opposite of alternative hypotheses and are logical devices used for statistical purposes. Here are three examples using the three kinds of relationships described above.

- There is no association between type of human service agency and its location in urban, suburban, or rural communities.
- There is no difference in average I.Q. scores between men and women.
- There is no correlation between income and years of schooling.

Now we get Hegelian, but we will return to the twentieth century in a moment. If we negate the negation, or reject the null hypothesis, then we must accept the alternative hypothesis. In other words, if we reject the above statements as false, then the relationships are real. The notion of rejecting the null hypothesis is important to the concept of statistical significance.

4.1.5 Significance

In statistics there is only one way to reject the null hypothesis—when the odds favor rejection. As we mentioned before, there are no laboratory controls over human subjects. Therefore, the authoritativeness of statistical results must be based on probability. *Significance* means that the odds favor a demonstrated relationship being real as opposed to being chance.

Recall the proverbial normal curve? We need to look at

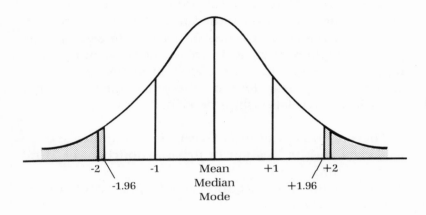

FIGURE 4.1 The Normal Curve

it for a moment in order to understand this concept. Refer to Figure 4.1.

If you dropped a bucket of sand on the floor, it would look something like this. Most of the grains of sand would pile up in the middle. The odds of any single grain of sand ending up at the very edge of either end are very small. Now think of each grain of sand as a case with a measurable value. The *normal curve* is a theoretical distribution of cases in which the mean, median, and mode are the same and in which distances from the mean can be measured in standardized distances such as standard deviation units or z-scores. *Z-scores* are standardized values transformed from distributions that are not distributed normally. The standardized units can be translated into percentages of the total distribution. For example, all the cases or grains of sand found within plus or minus 2 standard-deviation units from the mean would encompass about 95% of all the sand, with about 2.5% of the sand remaining at each end. Distributions which are not normal are said to be skewed. *Skewness* refers to values that are not symmetrical, are not found in equal numbers on either side of the mean.

Now we get to the point. Statistics are often used for detecting relationships among variables. *All relational, statistical computations result in numbers translatable to positions on the curve that are used to express the odds of those relationships being real rather than due to chance.*

By convention, the null hypothesis is rejected when the odds are equal to or greater than 95% that the relationship is real or, conversely, when the odds are equal to or less than 5% that the relationship is due to chance. This is referred to as the *confidence level.* We are sure you have seen this symbol in tables: P < .05. It means that the probability (P) is less than (<) 5 out of 100 (.05) that the demonstrated relationship is due to chance. That 5% region of the normal curve is called the *area of rejection,* or sometimes *alpha.* The other 95% is called the *area of acceptance,* sometimes referred to as *beta.*

4.1.6 One-Tail/Two-Tail

The *tail* is either of the two extreme ends of the curve, and the term is used to describe the *direction* of hypothesized relationships. Briefly, a *one-tail statistical test* hypothesizes a direction, while a *two-tail test* is directionless. For example, supposing we hypothesize that men and women will do equally well on a college entrance exam. That would be a two-tail test because there are two areas of rejection, one at either end of the normal curve; in other words, the men can either do better or worse and be statistically different from the women. However, if the confidence level is 5%, the result must fall within 2.5% of either end, as in Figure 4.2A.

In a one-tail test, we would begin by hypothesizing that one group would do better than the other. The 5% area of

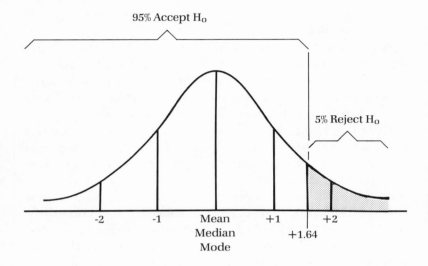

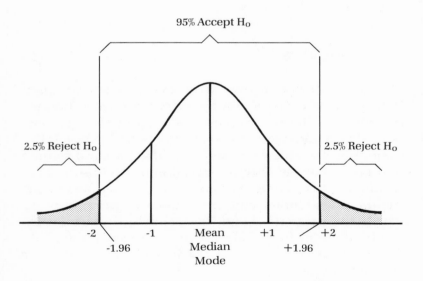

FIGURE 4.2 One-Tail and Two-Tail Statistical Tests

rejection would remain at one end, as in Figure 4.2B.

One-tail versus two-tail tests have always seemed to us a statistical anomaly. Direction is more information than difference and therefore more useful, but because of the smaller areas of rejection at either end of the distribution, directionless two-tail tests are more rigorous than one-tail tests. We recommend running all bivariate tests one-tail in order to avoid what are called Type 2 errors. We will explain the concept of Type 1 and Type 2 errors next.

4.1.7 Type 1/Type 2 Errors

Rejecting the null hypothesis when it is, in fact, true (no relationship) is a *Type 1 error*. Technically speaking, the area of rejection, or alpha, represents the odds of making a Type 1 error. Type 1 and Type 2 errors are important concepts to understand, but they do get rather convoluted, so we suggest memorizing the following sentence: *A Type 1 error is a spurious relationship.* You could also think of a Type 1 error as a *false positive*. That should make it easy to remember that a *Type 2 error* is a relationship that is overlooked.

Type 1 and Type 2 errors are particularly important to the setting of confidence levels. Let us set up an example. Suppose you are the program coordinator for a mental health clinic and you suspect the clinic's population is becoming more Hispanic. This would be an important trend because you would need to hire bilingual staff. However, staffing is a major decision, so you decide that unless the statistics you choose to measure the clinic's demographics show changes in significance at $P < .01$, you are going to conclude that your personal observations are due to chance.

In other words, you have decided that avoiding the wrong decision about staff is more important at the present time than overlooking changes in the clinic's population. By reducing the alpha to .01, you are not going to accept the change as real unless the odds are less than 1 in 100 that the change is due to chance. While you have reduced the possibility of making a Type 1 error, you have increased the odds of making a Type 2 error. Because you have decided to make the test so rigorous, the population could actually be changing although you would conclude it is not.

4.1.8 Parametric and Nonparametric Statistics

Nonparametric statistics are tests of a sample and they require only one thing from the data used in the test: a known number of cases. Further assumptions about the nature of the data are not required. Parametric tests are used to make inferences about a population with known parameters and they require that certain assumptions about the data be met. Those assumptions include normal distribution of the data and interval-level measurement. Parametric statistics are more powerful than nonparametric tests only when those assumptions are met. They are not superior to or more accurate than nonparametric tests.

4.1.9 Degrees of Freedom and Statistical Power

Degrees of freedom (abbreviated DF) is not an easy concept to explain, but essentially, it refers to the power of a statistical test. Degrees of freedom is somewhat difficult to conceptualize because it is determined differently depending on the level of measurement. With interval-level data, the more cases, the higher the degrees of freedom. It makes sense that the greater the number of cases, the greater the probability that a sample will represent its population. For categorical data and for crosstabulations, degrees of freedom is determined by the number of resulting data cells.

4.2 Crosstabulation

Crosstabulations—the first of the three ways to measure bivariate statistics—are used to display and analyze nominal, categorical data. Although we demonstrated in Chapter 1 how ordinal- and interval-level data can be collapsed into categories, such practices can weaken the power of statistical data analysis. An exception to this general rule would be to collapse higher levels of measurement into categories for descriptive purposes only.

The most commonly used statistical test for crosstabulation is the *chi-square*. The chi-square is based on a simple principle. Data are *expected* to arrange themselves in a particular pattern. However, *observed* data or frequencies usually deviate from the expected pattern. At some point (which is equal to statistical significance) the *observed frequencies deviate so much from expected frequencies that the demonstrated relationship probably is not due to chance.* Think about coin flipping with heads as one category and tails as the other. The more a coin is flipped, the more we would expect the distribution to be 50% heads and 50% tails. But suppose that the more times we flipped the coin, two times and then three times more heads came up than tails. There has to be something wrong with that coin or the way we are flipping it! At some point chance cannot be determining the outcome.

Before we get to an actual crosstabulation, we want to show you how this principle works with an example from the human services and how the chi-square can be a useful statistic for something as simple as a "one variable by n categories" analysis which we will demonstrate shortly. Suppose you are concerned that many psychiatric patients are hospitalized on weekends, but most hospital

M	Tu	W	Th	F	Sa	Su
10	5	5	6	8	6	10

FIGURE 4.3 Hospital Admissions by Days of the Week

staff work Monday through Friday. You go to the records and note the day of the week for the last 49 admissions. They break down as shown in Figure 4.3.

The expected frequency for each day of the week is seven (49 patients divided by seven days). Now for each cell, we are going to subtract the expected frequency from the observed frequency, square the difference, and divide by the expected frequency. The result is a chi-square ratio for each cell. Sum all the ratios and you have the total chi-square. This is the formula:

$$X^2 = \Sigma \ \frac{(O-E)^2}{E}$$

and this is the ratio for the first cell (Monday):

$$\frac{(10-7)^2}{7} = 1.29.$$

The total chi-square is 3.60. You may have noticed that it doesn't matter whether you subtract the observed or expected frequency, because the result is squared. In this procedure, degrees of freedom equal the number of cells minus one, which is 6 in our example. If you take off your shelf the dusty statistics books you bought as an undergraduate and look up the chi-square distribution table, you will see that our findings are nowhere near significant. So, for the time being, your hunch was wrong.

5	5
5	5

10	0
10	0

0	10
0	10

FIGURE 4.4 Crosstabulation: Independence

Notice how the chi-square takes into account the accumulative effect of the observed minus expected frequencies for each cell. Let's look at the above example and see how that might be interpreted. It's obvious Monday and Sunday contributed the most. Is there something unique about Mondays and Sundays that bears watching in the future? Does the weekend send people over the edge, so that they show up at admissions late Sunday or Monday?

Now let's look at more complicated crosstabulations and how to interpret them. When we test for the association between two characteristics or variables, we are testing for independence versus dependence. *Independence* means no relationship. *Dependence* means some relationship or linkage between the two variables.

What does independence look like? Suppose we have two variables with 20 subjects arranged in a 2 × 2 crosstabulation. (Let's not identify the variables, but concentrate on the distribution only.) All the illustrations in Figure 4.4 are examples of independence. In Crosstabulation A, there is nothing going on. All the observed frequencies equal the expected frequencies. There is complete independence between the row variable and the column variable. In this instance, chi-square equals zero.

By convention, the row variable is the independent variable and the column variable is the dependent variable. In Crosstabulations B and C, there is no variance in

10	0
0	10

0	10
10	0

FIGURE 4.5 Crosstabulation: Dependence

the column variable. Thus, all the subjects, as measured by the dependent variable, think the same, look the same, or whatever. Independence again.

Some of you reading this are probably thinking, "But according to the chi-square formula you provided, there are still discrepancies between the observed and the expected that the chi-square will detect." That is true. However, the chi-square formula for crosstabulation is adjusted to take that into account. Look it up in that dusty book we mentioned. The principle remains the same: the discrepancies between observed and expected frequencies are not statistically significant.

Examples of statistical dependence are found in Figure 4.5. In both examples, something is definitely going on. There is something about being in a row category that is associated with being in a column category. The observed frequencies do not equal the expected frequencies.

Let us finish this section with a live example and a somewhat larger crosstabulation. Unmarried, pregnant teens can either keep their babies, place them for adoption, or have an abortion. We hypothesize that the decision is related to religious background. We identify a sizable maternity population at a local hospital. Conveniently, 50 are Catholic, 50 are Jewish, and 50 are Protestant. Their decisions are found in Table 4.1. In this case, the degrees of freedom equal the number of row cells minus 1 times the

TABLE 4.1 Religious Background by Maternity Decision

Religious Background	Decision		
	Keep	*Place*	*Abort*
Catholic	25	20	5
Jewish	20	25	5
Protestant	20	20	10

Chi-square = 4.5, DF = 4, N.S. (Not Significant)

number of column cells minus 1, or (3–1) times (3–1), which equals 4. The results are not significant. But, if you looked at the data and thought, "There is obviously nothing going on there," you would be partly right and partly wrong. There is nothing going on as far as chi-square is concerned. There is no association between religious background and the women's decisions. However, on the whole they are not having many abortions, and that may be worth pursuing depending on your interests and purpose. *Just because data is not statistically significant doesn't mean it isn't interesting!*

One postscript concerning the chi-square: no more than 20% of the expected frequencies can be less than 5. That is because empty cells skew the results.

There are two other interesting statistical tests used with categorical data. *Fisher's exact text* is similar to the chi-square, but is used with very small samples, especially when small samples produce too many empty cells as described above. *Lambda* measures the probability that any one case will fall into a certain category if the category from the other variable is known. Lambda ranges from zero to one. In Figure 4.4 the example on the left would have a lambda of 0. In Figure 4.5 both examples would have a lambda of 1.0. A lambda of .5 or better should be

TABLE 4.2 Gender, Degree, and Salary of Ten College Graduates

Gender	Degree	Starting Salary	Five Years Later
Male	B.A.	12,000	14,000
Female	Master's	16,000	21,000
Male	Ph.D.	20,000	30,000
Female	B.A.	13,000	14,000
Male	Master's	16,000	20,000
Female	Ph.D.	23,000	30,000
Male	B.A.	12,000	15,000
Female	Master's	17,000	25,000
Male	Ph.D.	21,000	29,000
Female	B.A.	11,000	16,000

worth interpreting. Both the Fisher's exact test and lambda are available with SPSS-X.

4.3 Comparing Central Tendency

Comparing central tendency refers to looking for differences between two groups by (1) comparing the group means with interval-level data or comparing the group medians with ordinal-level data, and (2) comparing the dispersion or spread around the group means or medians. The purpose is to search for statistically significant differences, that is, differences between groups that are so great they are not likely to result from chance. Take a look at the raw data in Table 4.2. There are ten cases and four variables. Each case represents a college graduate, his or her gender, degree attained, starting salary after college, and salary five years later. The aim is to look for differences in salary that can be attributed to gender and level of education.

For this analysis, we are going to begin with the *student's t-test,* a statistic for comparing the means of two samples or comparing a sample mean with its population

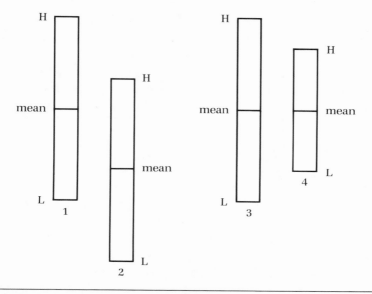

FIGURE 4.6 Group Mean Comparisons

mean. As a matter of fact, you can only compare two means by using the *t*-test. The *t*-test is essentially a ratio of the difference between means divided by what is called the estimated standard error of difference, that is, the size of the variance around the means. Conceptually, the larger the difference between the means and the smaller the variance in both groups, the larger the *t*. Look at Figure 4.6.

There are four groups represented by a vertical bar. Each group has a mean and a range from the lowest score (L) to the highest score (H). If we compare Group 1 with Group 2, it is obvious that the means are different and, despite the variances being equal, the extreme scores are different and, therefore, there is a good chance that *t* will be significant. However *t* cannot be significant between

Groups 3 and 4 because the means are identical.

To see how the *t*-test works, let's begin by comparing two sample means, a procedure sometimes referred to as a *groupwise comparison*. Using the raw data in Table 4.2, let's define gender as an independent variable consisting of two classes of groups, male and female. The starting salary after college will be the dependent variable. The null hypothesis states that there is no difference in starting salary between men and women. The mean starting salary for men is \$16,200, for women \$16,000. The degrees of freedom for the *t*-test equal the number of cases minus the number of samples, in this case $10 - 2 = 8$.

Before we go on, we want to take a moment to comment on the *t*-test and sample size. It's fairly evident that a difference of \$16,200 and \$16,000 is not significant. In fact, $P = .95$. So in this case, differences in salary are not attributable to gender. However, as the degrees of freedom increase, that \$200 difference will become significant at $P = .05$ at some point. Technically speaking, degrees of freedom correlate positively with the chance of making a Type 1 error (a spurious relationship). As we have said before, statistics can distort as well as explain. There are two things you can do about very large numbers of cases. You can get a book by Jacob Cohen called *Statistical Power Analysis* (1977) and learn how to interpret the "effect size" of a relationship as well as its statistical significance. A more immediate solution would be to reduce the *N* by instructing the computer to select a random sample of your sample for the *t*-test statistic.[1]

Now, let's look at what is called a *pairwise comparison*. In this case, we simply compare the mean of one variable with the mean of another. Suppose we want to know if the increase in salary between college graduation and five years later is statistically significant. It turns out that the

---

[1]The procedure is called SAMPLE in SPSS-X; it is not available with SAS.

mean at Time 1 for all the subjects is $16,100, and $21,400 at Time 2, a mean increase of $5,300, and that $t = 5.76$, significant at P < .01. We reject the null hypothesis of no difference and conclude that the passage of time has indeed contributed to significant increases in salaries.

What if we wanted to go beyond a simple pairwise comparison and compare the salaries of the B.A. graduates with the M.A.'s and the Ph.D.'s? Because there are more than two categories within one characteristic, the t-test will not suffice. For that analysis, we need to use analysis of variance (ANOVA), which can get complicated when one wants to measure interaction effects, for example, the relative influences of multiple characteristics. For that reason, ANOVA has a separate chapter of its own—Chapter 8.

We have been using interval-level data (money) for our illustration of the bivariate t-test. But what if the dependent variable were ordinal-level of measurement? Suppose the same college graduates were rating their overall education as poor, fair, or good both at graduation and five years later. For group comparisons, use the nonparametric *Mann-Whitney U*. For paired comparisons, use a nonparametric one-way analysis of variance.[2]

4.4 Correlation

Correlation is probably the linchpin of statistics. Without it there wouldn't be much to talk about. In this section we want to explain briefly what correlation is, how to use it, and demonstrate the use of the most common correlation statistics. As a matter of fact, you may find this section rather brief for so important a topic. That's because we left the more technical aspects of correlation for the discussions on multiple correlations.

---

[2]Both are available with SPSS-X and SAS.

As we explained earlier, a *correlation* is a relationship in which the values of one characteristic fluctuate or vary with the values of another. This assumes ordering, so only ordinal- and interval-level data are appropriate.

The most commonly used correlation statistic is the parametric test, Pearson's product moment coefficient, or *Pearson's r*. Calculating r results in a value from -1.00 (perfect negative correlation) to 0.00 (no relationship) to 1.00 (perfect positive correlation).

Let's go back and look at Table 4.2. Suppose we want to test the relationship between salary after graduation and salary five years later. We are hypothesizing that those who start ahead stay ahead and those who start behind stay behind. It turns out that $r = .96$, almost a perfect positive correlation. Pearson's r can then be converted to a z—score for purposes of interpreting statistical significance. In this case, the probability of the relationship being due to chance is practically nonexistent, something like $P = .0001$. In our opinion, Pearson's r tends to be too robust a statistic. Many times an r of $+/-.20$ can be statistically significant. We recommend that an r closer to zero than $+/-.50$ be interpreted as "suggestive."

An often overlooked aspect of bivariate analysis is the *partial correlation*. This is a spurious relationship that results from a powerful correlation within a certain subgroup. For example, suppose the positive relationship between starting salary and salary five years later was real for the men, but not for the women. Pearson's r could still be significant if the data within the male subgroup were influential enough.

An easy way to deal with this problem is to run the correlations for each subgroup one at a time. In our example, even though the N for each test is reduced to 5, the relationships are still strong enough for a high correlation and for statistical significance. For the men $r = .99$, $P = .002$, and for the women, $r = .94$, $P = .02$. Remember we said that r was a robust test? $P = .02$ with 5 cases!

Two common nonparametric tests of correlation are *Spearman's rho* and *Kendall's tau*. Spearman's rho is often used when one variable is interval-level data and the other is ordinal or when both variables are ordinal. However, results from rho tend to wash out when there are a lot of duplicate values in the data. For example, too many identical judgments of Poor (coded for the computer as the number 2) in one variable with judgments of Fair (coded as a 3) in a second variable. For those circumstances, Kendall's tau is a better test. Both tests are available with SPSS-X and SAS.

4.5 Steps in the Bivariate Data Analysis

Before going on to more number-crunching mayhem, we want to provide you with a framework for bivariate or two-characteristic analysis. The purpose is twofold: we want to help you get what there is to get from bivariate analysis and then identify those important relationships that are suitable for multivariate analyses.

So far you have collected some numbers, cleaned the data, and described it using various statistics and graphic displays. Now what? Well, this is how we conduct a bivariate analysis.

- Determine the level of measurement of your data.
- Determine whether your data are parametric or nonparametric.
- Knowing that you can only crosstabulate, compare central tendency, or correlate, sort out the variables accordingly and test every conceivable bivariate relationship.
- Identify clusters of statistically significant relationships that appear to logically relate to one another.
- With the relationships most important to your purpose, test for subgroup variations.
- Watch out for Type 2 errors.

TABLE 4.3 Bivariate Variable List

Nominal		Ordinal		Interval	
Independent	*Dependent*	*Independent*	*Dependent*	*Independent*	*Dependent*
VAR A	VAR B	VAR D	VAR D	VAR E	VAR E
VAR B	VAR C	VAR E	VAR E	VAR F	VAR F
VAR C		VAR F	VAR F	VAR G	VAR G
		VAR G	VAR G	VAR H	VAR H
				VAR I	VAR I
				VAR J	VAR J

- Formulate more complicated relationships for multivariate testing.

Now let's go over these steps in more detail.

4.5.1 Determine Level of Measurement

Begin by making six lists of variables organized by level of measurement (nominal/ordinal/interval). Then logically assign each variable to an independent variable list and/or a dependent variable list. *Do not hesitate to duplicate.* At this point we are worrying about Type 2 errors, that is, overlooking something important. Later on we will worry about generating a lot of garbage. If you are not sure whether a characteristic is properly ordinal- or interval-level data, put it in both groups. If you are not sure whether a variable is properly independent or dependent (or you are positive it is merely associative), put it in both groups. You will end up with something like Table 4.3.

4.5.2 Determine Parametric Versus Nonparametric

For the most part, the interval-level data is parametric, the rest is not. You can usually assume the interval-level data meets the assumptions for parametric tests unless

TABLE 4.4 Sample Bivariate Statistics by Level of Measurement and Type of Relationship Hypothesized

Variables		Type of Relationship		
Independent	*Dependent*	*Association*	*Difference*	*Correlation*
Nominal	Nominal	chi-square		
Nominal	Ordinal	chi-square	Mann-Whitney	
Nominal	Interval		*t*	
Ordinal	Nominal	chi-square	Mann-Whitney	
Ordinal	Ordinal	chi-square	one-way ANOVA	tau/rho
Ordinal	Interval		one-way ANOVA	tau/rho
Interval	Nominal		*t*	
Interval	Ordinal		one-way ANOVA	tau/rho
Interval	Interval		*t*	*r*

there are problems with the original sample, that is, that the data were not selected randomly from a larger population. This should not be a problem, however, if you are careful about how far you generalize the results. You can use parametric statistics with any interval-level data if your interpretations are limited to the cases used in the tests.

4.5.3 Test Everything

Now run everything with everything, a technique sometimes referred to as the "all-by-all" analysis. Consult Table 4.4 for sample statistics for every possible combination of bivariate relationships. Choose the appropriate test by determining (1) the level of measurement for each variable, (2) which variable is independent and which variable is dependent, and (3) whether you are testing for an association, a difference in central tendency, or a correlation (or all three).

4.5.4 Identify Significant Clusters

Out of hundreds (or thousands if you are up to it) of possible relationships, begin to list those statistically significant relationships that (1) are most important to your purpose and/or (2) logically appear to relate to one another. Obviously, depending on your major purposes, some nonsignificant relationships may be even more important.

4.5.5 Subgroup Variation

At this point you should have a pretty good idea about what you have. Now identify those subgroups important to your purposes and test for their effects. For example, if your analysis of the data in Table 4.2 shows there is no relationship between gender and income or between race and income, what about the relation between income and black males? This process could go on forever, but there are two natural limits: the first is your interest and the second is sample size. The more the data are carved up, the fewer cases left to analyze.

4.5.6 Type 1 Errors

So far we have been worrying about overlooking something important, that is, Type 2 errors. Now it is time to consider all the garbage that has been generated. If you set your confidence level for statistical significance at .05, then for every 100 tests there should be 5 statistically significant relationships that result from chance alone. If you have no more than 5% of all possible relationships statistically significant, you may have a pile of useless results. If you have 20% or more, great. This should be easy if you were at all judicious with your original variable list.

Supposing you have about 10% of your relationships significant at .05, how would you know the results are valid? An easy technique is to look for examples of *concur-*

rent and *discriminant validity* in the data. Look for things
that should correlate and do (concurrent validity). Two
ideas come to mind: pairs of similar variables that correlate in the same direction and pairs of opposites that correlate negatively. Look for things that do correlate, but appear odd and may result from random events (a lack of
discriminant validity).

4.5.7 Generate Multivariate Hypotheses

Suppose you have determined that gender and race predict income or that intelligence and motivation predict
success in psychotherapy, but you do not know which of
the independent variables are the most important and by
how much. What if the most interesting variables are at
different levels of measurement? What do you do then?
Unfortunately, many people never get to multivariate
tests in a statistical data analysis. Most analyses end with
bivariate tests. But some of the most interesting information comes from multivariate analysis, which is the subject of the second half of this book.

CHAPTER 5

Reliability

We need to turn away from results and interpretation for a moment and consider the nature of the raw data. If there was something wrong with the manner in which information was collected in the first place, the outcome is meaningless. We need to determine if the data collection instruments were reliable. By *reliability,* we mean consistency of measurement over time or consistency of result in repeated measures.

Suppose you have a desk in front of you and a tape measure. Using the tape measure, you determine that the desk is 40 inches long. You then fold up the tape measure, put it away, take it out again, and measure the desk a second time. More than likely the desk is still 40 inches long, a good indication that the tape measure is a reliable instrument.

There are, essentially, two relevant applications of this principle to the human services. They are inter-rater reliability and inter-item reliability.

5.1 Inter-Rater Reliability

Of the two, *inter-rater reliability* is the easier to understand and the easier to measure statistically. For example, think about studying family interaction by observing family therapy sessions through a one-way mirror. We are interested in the concept of cohesion and have decided that the more often family members interrupt one another, the less cohesive they are as a family. (Whether or

not interruption is an indication of cohesiveness constitutes a validity problem, not a reliability problem, but assume, for the moment, that interruptions measure cohesiveness.) There are two judges observing the family with
a checklist that contains various possibilities of one family
member interrupting another. After the session, the
judges compare notes and discover they agree on eight interruptions and disagree on two. The inter-rater reliability is 80%, probably sufficient for most research, but anything less would not be acceptable.

Reliability is always expressed as a percentage. One
hundred percent means absolute agreement or consistency. Zero would mean the data were collected randomly. In the above example, if a third judge filled out the
checklist without observing the family, any agreement
with the other judges would have to result from chance.

Notice we said agreement or consistency, not accuracy.
It is possible to be entirely consistent and entirely wrong.
One hundred people can all agree that the world is flat.
Technically speaking, it is possible for a measurement to
be reliable but not valid. It is not possible, however, for a
measurement to be valid but not reliable.

What would contribute to problems in inter-rater reliability? Poor judgment, obviously, possibly resulting
from poor training, but the cause could also be problems
in the operational definitions. In the above example, if the
judges did not understand or could not agree on what con-
stituted an interruption, they could not agree on how
many interruptions they observed.

5.2 Inter-Item Reliability

Inter-item reliability applies to judgments made regarding
items on a test or scales on a questionnaire. Rather than a
measurement of agreement between judges, this kind of
reliability is a measure of the correlation of individual

items on a scale. There are three common ways to test inter-item reliability: *test-retest, split-half,* and *correlation between items.*

5.2.1 Test-Retest

If people take a test twice, the two scores should correlate. Those who do well the first time should do well the second. They won't do exactly the same, because familiarity with the test should help them do a little better. In this application, test-retest can be measured by Pearson's r. Pearson's r should be .90 or higher for good reliability. This procedure is the best choice when there are two separate data collection points.

5.2.2 Split-Half

The next two tests of reliability, split-half and correlation between items, are used when data are collected only once, usually in the form of scales that, because of some conceptual framework, contain items that logically should relate to one another. The measurement task is to establish whether there is *internal consistency.* For example, let's consider a teacher who is making some judgments regarding child development in a preschool program. She selects two instruments, both of which claim to measure child development. Both contain several items that are similar. The teacher's ratings of two children's ability to make friends and engage in games are illustrated in Table 5.1. Notice that the teacher is the same, the items are similar, but the instruments are different.

According to both instruments, Mary can make friends and play games with other children better than John can. In the first instrument, making friends and playing games correlate positively. Even though John and Mary do not have the same abilities, it makes sense that, in general, the

TABLE 5.1 Reliability As Internal Consistency: Two Instruments of Teacher Judgments of Child Development

	First Instrument	
	Making Friends	*Playing Games*
John	4	5
Mary	6	7
	Second Instrument	
	Making Friends	*Playing Games*
John	4	5
Mary	7	6

more any child can make friends, the easier it is to engage in playing games and vice versa. The second instrument lacks this internal logic and, therefore, appears to be less reliable. For some reason, making friends and playing games correlates positively for John and negatively for Mary. For whatever reason, the first instrument shows reliable inter-item correlation and the second does not.

Split-half reliability is determined by dividing the items on an instrument into two parts and then correlating the two parts. The *Spearman-Brown* is a commonly used test for this procedure. Statistical corrections can be made when the number of items are uneven. The resulting statistic ranges from zero to one.

Split-half reliability lends itself well to applications whereby items can be split on logical parameters. For example, suppose the instruments that measure child development in Table 5.1 contain items that are logical opposites. Making friends would correlate negatively with social isolation, for example, while engaging in games would correlate negatively with bullying or hyper-competitiveness.

5.2.3 Correlation Between Items

This last procedure for determining inter-item reliability measures the average correlation of all items under analysis. The specific test is the old reliable of reliability, *Cronbach's alpha*. Alpha is a general purpose, conservative test of the lower limits of internal consistency. An alpha of .8 or higher is sufficient for most research in the human services. Alpha is sensitive to the number of items under analysis. As the number of items increases, the value of alpha increases (although with diminishing returns).

All the statistical procedures mentioned in this chapter can be found in SPSS-X.

CHAPTER 6

Relationships Among More Than Two Characteristics

At this point, it gets more interesting and, consequently, much more complicated. In the first half of the book, we were only interested in finding and describing relationships between two characteristics, but now we want to explore relationships that go beyond description and begin to explain. For that we need to use multivariate statistics.

6.1 Why Use Multivariate Statistics?

As we discussed in earlier chapters, most things important to the study of human beings cannot be explained adequately by two characteristics or variables at a time. Before there was easy access to sophisticated, computerized statistical packages, it was common for researchers to select two variables—one defined as the dependent or outcome variable and the other defined as the independent or causal variable—postulate a relationship between them, and, then test that relationship for statistical significance or, alternatively, identify a plethora of presumed independent variables and then test a series of paired relationships one at a time.

There are several problems with this procedure. The odds of finding something worthwhile within a reasonable amount of time are remote. Secondly, rarely does the variation in one characteristic simply and obviously explain the variation in another. For the moment, let's consider the relationship between age and height. Those two variables are chosen for this example because there is a known relationship between them. A 12-year-old is normally taller than a 6-year-old and shorter than a 16-year-old, a statistically measurable hypothesis. However, the relationship is not perfect. The correlation between increasing age and increasing height disappears as people grow older. Indeed, not only are 16-year-olds often taller than 65-year-olds, but many people in their 60s and 70s are shorter than they were when they were younger.

If, as a researcher, you wanted to predict future height from present height and age, you would be more likely to be successful if you had access to information about gender, whether the individual was large- or small-boned, and perhaps the height and age of relatives. If you tested the relationship of each of these variables individually to height, you would undoubtedly find some of those relationships to be statistically significant. However, if you tested the relationship between each of the additional variables excluding age and height, you would also undoubtedly find that some of them were related.

Since the laws of probability state that in a series of analyses some relationships will be significant by chance, some of your results will be spurious. The other problem you will face is interaction effects. In a paired or bivariate analysis, you cannot calculate the interrelationship between height and age with gender, and all variables are treated as though they were independent of one another—which most parents and teachers of adolescents would agree is not true. Although some of the bivariate techniques discussed in earlier chapters allow for the statistical control of interaction effects, this becomes increasingly cumbersome as more and more variables are added to the series of analyses. The results also become increasingly difficult to interpret.

A basic assumption behind the use of multivariate statistical analyses is that most variables we can measure, whether from surveys, questionnaires, standardized tests, or observations, are at best partial measurements of the underlying variables of interest. Although age, years of education, and income, are fixed and measurable at any given point in time, they are probably not what we want to discover in a study of single mothers. Variables such as self-esteem, depression level, anxiety, knowledge of child development, or parenting capacity are measured much less completely, even by the most sophisticated, validated, and reliable scale. Yet all may be part of what we need to know to predict the ability of a single parent to raise a physically and emotionally healthy child.

Some variables may measure overlapping parts of the same underlying construct. For example, education and income are predictive of each other to some degree. In the question of predicting the ability of a single parent to provide an adequate home, a 17-year-old high school dropout living on public assistance may have lower self-esteem, less knowledge of child development, and lower parenting capacity than a 35-year-old professional woman with a good income, a supportive family, and household help. Between these extremes, multivariate techniques can help to determine the relative influence of the variables and the degree to which they are interrelated or correlated.

Now let's consider a specific study relevant to the human services (DiLeonardi, 1979) to illustrate how paired comparisons can obscure relationships or lead to false conclusions. Our example is a study of the incidence of child abuse by community areas in a large city. Paired analyses of median income, density (measured as thousands of people per square mile), percentage of the population receiving public assistance, median family income, and child abuse rates revealed strong and statistically significant correlations. Ignoring other theoretically meaningful comparisons (such as unemployment rate, number of single parent families, and alcoholism or drug abuse rate, all of which could be reasonably argued to be important in such a sociological analysis) one or two of the computed significant correlations could form persuasive arguments to support one or more of the current theories of relationship to or, if not careful in interpretation, causes of, child abuse.

Using a multivariate correlational technique—multiple regression analysis (see Chapter 7)—the child abuse rate (quantified as the number of reported cases per 1,000 children in order to control for the differing numbers of children in various community areas) became the dependent or *outcome variable*, and all of the others became independent or *predictor variables*. All of the associated variables in the study that were chosen as "predictors"—income, public assistance rate, and density—measured part of the same underlying factor, which might be characterized as "urban poverty population." The density variable had the highest value and the highest significance level, but at a correlation of .80, when squared, explained only 64% of the variance in abuse rates, a respectable but not astounding result, since it still left 36% of the variance unexplained. However, the full regression equation, the one containing all the variables, explained very little more than density alone. Had the researcher chosen to use income alone or public assistance status alone as the independent variable because of strong theoretical beliefs and used a bivariate technique, statistical support would have been given to an incomplete and possibly spurious relationship.

6.2 Multivariate Techniques

There are a great many multivariate techniques available to anyone who has access to computer facilities at a university, all of which have statistical software available. In the past few years, major statistical software producers have developed scaled-down versions of the most popular techniques for home computers. This ready availability has meant that anyone who can read instructions can perform many analyses. The most common difficulties are deciding which technique to use and how to interpret the results. This book concentrates on the most commonly used and useful techniques—multiple regression analysis, analysis of variance, and factor analysis—and on two techniques of particular interest to the human services, in which many variables of interest are nominal in level—discriminant function analysis, which has a nominal-level classification variable, and log linear analysis, which is a useful form of analysis of multiple nominal-level variables.

Each of these techniques will be described at greater length in the chapter devoted to it. Here we will only contrast them and talk about general assumptions and limitations underlying their use. Since this book is an overview for people with limited statistical background and probably even less interest in hand calculation and mathematical theory, we will not explain the mathematical basis nor offer the accompanying equations, which form the foundation for a true understanding of the logic of each technique. We will present the simplest form of each technique that will make it accessible to the nonmathematical user and try to help you steer clear of common pitfalls.

We urge you to try each of the techniques discussed here on data with which you have become familiar through your own theoretical and practical knowledge of the subject and on which you have used descriptive and bivariate techniques. In this way you will be able to discover what is useful, what is not, and what may need further examination. For those of you who are ready for a more comprehensive examination of each technique or have more questions, there are references in each chapter.

6.2.1 Multiple Regression Analysis

Multiple regression analysis (MRA) is a very widely used (and misused) technique. It allows researchers to select predictor or independent variables that they assume to be related to a dependent, or criterion, or outcome, variable (here, all three mean the same thing). They also choose an appropriate model to determine the relative importance of the predictor variables.

The method of introducing variables into a regression model, or equation, is called the *inclusion method.* Its two most commonly used forms are *hierarchial inclusion,* where the researcher decides that some variables are more important than others and therefore should be tested in the equation first, and *stepwise inclusion,* where the computer tests the relative statistical strength of each paired comparison and enters them into the equation in strict numerical order.

With either inclusion method, once a variable has been entered into the model, each succeeding variable is selected for how much additional variance in the criterion variable it explains, not how much it explains independently. In the child abuse study described above, after density was entered, public assistance rates did not add enough additional information after income levels were entered to become part of the solution, even though in a paired comparison with abuse rates, the correlation was both high and significant. If the researcher had had a strong belief that Public Assistance Rate was the key variable, she would have used hierarchical inclusion and entered public assistance rate into the model before allowing density or income to be considered. It is because of the many key decisions like this—based on the nature of the problem, the theoretical stance, or the hypotheses in the study—that it is said that statistics is more of an art than a science.

6.2.2 Analysis of Variance

Analysis of variance (ANOVA) is a method of statistical analysis in which one or more nominal-level classification variables are used to establish groups in which one or more independent interval level variables are examined for differences among the groups. It is used both for two variables and for more. It is a research design as well as a tool for data analysis.

Studies of college faculty, for example, may use analysis of variance to determine whether gender, experience, publication record or education are determining factors in achieving rank or tenure. One of the sometimes-overlooked difficulties with its use is that it has an assumption of roughly equivalent numbers of cases in each of the categories. If this is not the case in your sample, results must be examined with caution. Although especially useful when looking at two variables or to examine the results and relative strength of covariates, it gives less information about the strength of multiple variables in relationship to each other and to the criterion or dependent variable than do some of the other techniques.

Covariates are variables in the problem you are studying which may measure some part of the same underlying dimension as the variable is which you are most interested. Thus, they vary at the same rate or in the same direction as your independent variable, or "co-vary."

6.2.3 Factor Analysis

The third technique for analyzing the effects of more than two variables that we will look at is *factor analysis*. This is quite different from multiple regression analysis both in its requirements for use and in the kind of information that can be gained from it. The major difference is the absence of any formulation of dependence and independence or predictor and criterion. Factor analysis helps us to find the underlying structure of the data, to determine which combinations of variables tend to occur together.

It is often used as a data-reduction technique, such as in a study that has collected 200 items of information on a number of people, such as a broad survey on life satisfaction or on spending patterns. *Data reduction* is a term for a way of using fewer variables to represent the important characteristics in your analysis. Many of the questions—such as what are the respondents' hobbies, what do they do with their leisure time, and do they spend money at sporting goods stores, use the library, attend concerts or plays, or belong to a health club—may be measuring different but overlapping parts of a dimension or factor that we could call Use of Leisure or Activity/Passivity. If the overall purpose of the study is to see how a number of life choices—including marital status, socialization, job or career choice, salary, childbearing status, peer relationships, family relationships, and leisure time activities—affect life satisfaction, it would be clearer and more convenient to use a single factor of active-to-passive leisure style in the final analysis than to use 15 variables that each measure different parts of this dimension. In the analysis, some variables, and the factors on which they occur strongly, or "load," assume so little importance that they may be discarded. Factor analysis allows you to use the *factor scores* themselves in further analysis rather than the several variables represented on them.

Like multiple regression, factor analysis has an assumption of interval-level data, with the possibility of using some dichotomous dummy variables. Some experts in the field also feel that ordinal-level variables may be used with caution.

6.2.4 Discriminant Function Analysis

The fourth technique to be covered, *discriminant function analysis,* is really a special case of multiple regression, although the coefficient for each variable, the function scores cannot be interpreted in the same way as their counterpart regression weights. The advantage of using discriminant function analysis is that it allows the selection of a nominal-level classification variable and measures the relative importance of a number of interval-level variables in distinguishing each of the nominal categories from one another.

It is useful, for example, in studying the differences between homebound and active elderly or recidivists and nonrecidivists in studies of mental patients or delinquents; differences in work activities of social workers with BSW, MSW, and Ph.D. degrees; and differences among victims of physical abuse, sexual abuse, and neglect; or any of a myriad or other situations where the crux of the problem is to look at what variables might distinguish different categories of people or problems.

6.2.5 Log Linear Analysis

The last technique we will explore, *log linear analysis,* is one of the more recently developed multivariate techniques. Like the other techniques, it involves developing a model that postulates the relationship between several variables and testing it to see how well it fits the data collected. The way in which it does this is not unlike factor analysis in that the computer tries successive proposed patterns of relationships until it comes as close as possible to the actual relationship found in the data. The strong advantage of log linear analysis (and other analyses of cross classifications) is that it is designed for use with all nominal-level data, unlike the other techniques mentioned here. Also unlike the other techniques, the researcher must postulate the specifications of the model, the way in which he believes the variables are related to each other. Cross-classification techniques are most useful when there are a large number of cases, distributed so that most possible combinations are present.

6.3 Basic Assumptions

Every statistical test is a logical extension of certain underlying assumptions. Among the assumptions peculiar to each test are some regarding the sampling procedure, the level of measurement of the data, the shape of the underlying distribution, and often a minimum sample size for which the technique is effective and powerful enough to detect real differences. The value and validity of multivariate statistical analysis are greatest when the underlying assumptions on which the techniques were developed are met. Specific requirements for each technique will be discussed in the chapter on that technique.

Many of the most powerful statistical techniques assume continuous interval-level data, which has equal intervals between points and the possibility of intermediate values and something approaching the distribution of the normal curve because of this underlying continuity. (See Chapters 1 and 4 for amplification on this point.)

The normal curve is that familiar shape mentioned earlier that is like an inverted "u" with the ends stretched out in both directions. It indicates that whatever we are measuring, such as age, income, or test scores, is normally distributed. That means that most cases or people fall in the middle, that equal numbers fall on either side of the middle, and that the farther from the midpoint on either end, the fewer of them there are. A sample or group hardly ever actually forms a perfect normal curve when it is plotted on graph paper. However, the normal curve is the theoretical distribution on which the most common probability statistics are based. For a more comprehensive explanation, see one of the basic statistics texts in the list of references. The general statistics texts demonstrate mathematically that if a sufficient number of independent random samples of adequate size are drawn from a population, the distribution of their means will approach the normal curve. It is this extension that allows us to use probability statistics on samples that themselves may not be as symmetrical as a normal distribution.

This brings us to the point at issue for working with multivariate techniques. The basic assumption for use with multiple regression, factor analysis, and other techniques is of a multivariate normal distribution. If you were to take graph paper and plot the income of your sample, you might possibly get a normal distribution. This is less likely if you plotted their age or education, because age is not normally distributed in the population at large, and there are probably fewer adults in a country with mandatory schooling who have only a first-grade education than who have a graduate degree. If you tried to combine even these three characteristics and especially if you were interested in more about them than that, you could not plot each case on a two-dimensional piece of paper. The multidimensional equivalent of the normal curve is a strictly theoretical distribution known as a *multivariate normal distribution,* and it would look somewhat like a flying saucer, with an approximately normal distribution for each variable.

The assumption of a multivariate normal distribution requires the use of interval-level data because it can take any of a number of values or points between them on a continuous line and can be used in any mathematical computation. The one exception is the careful use of a limited number of *dummy variables,* dichotomous yes-no or zero-one variables that indicate the presence or absence of some characteristic. Although they have no intermediate points, they can serve quite well as part of a multivariate data set. There may be difficulty with their use in certain circumstances, which will be discussed in the individual chapters on each technique.

The question of sample size is a key one, and one that is often ignored in studies in the human services. One rule of thumb for any multivariate technique is that there should be ten times as many cases as variables in the analysis. Therefore, if you are using age, income, education, gender, and ethnicity as variables in your study, you would need fifty cases before you even got into the meat of your study of depression or life satisfaction or achievement. In the above example, Gender would become one dummy variable. But if you wanted to look at the effects of ethnicity and you wanted to classify Black, White, and Hispanic, you would need three variables (Black vs. Not Black, White vs. Not White, and Hispanic vs. Not Hispanic) to represent ethnicity, with Other as the unnamed category (see Chapter 1) and by doing so would raise the number of variables needed to seven and the minimum number of cases to seventy. The less restrictive rule is that there must be at least fifty more cases than variables. When you think of the fact that most multivariate techniques are based on *matrix algebra* (whose purpose, simply speaking, is to see if there are unique relationships among the variables so that changes in one or more can predict changes in others), the relatively large ratio of cases to variables makes sense.

If you study matrix algebra, you will learn to add, subtract, multiply, and divide matrices, just as you learned to add, subtract, multiply, and divide whole numbers and fractions in elementary school. When you consider that each line, or row, in a matrix contains all the information on one case, and each column contains all the information for all cases on one variable, such as age or income, this has a potential for summarizing a great deal of information. If you have, as one recently published study did, 30 variables about 12 boys with which you attempt to develop some prediction for success in treatment, it is intuitively obvious that each of those 12 cases could easily be unique. Even if they are not, the likelihood that even 2 of those 12 vary in the same ways on several of the variables of interest is not high. With a sample of this size, clinical interpretation and qualitative analysis are probably much more valid because at least they don't have to deal with the difficulty of quantifying human characteristics, which we classify under measurement error, since even the best measure of depression or motivation is at best a partial representation of the reality.

6.4 Preparing Your Data for Analysis

Although it is always best to think through your analysis in advance and to collect your data at the highest possible level of measurement, there are still ways of changing the form of your data and the level of measurement before your analysis. This also involves planning, but may help you to rescue what looks like a bad situation. As discussed in Chapter 1, multiple category nominal-level variables such as Type of Social Service Setting can be changed into (K-1) dummy variables, one less than the number of categories in the original variable. This is a legitimate way to enhance the power of data to be used in multivariate techniques that have an assumption of interval-level data.

Another alternative that is sometimes possible is to change nominal data into interval-level data. An example is data collected on level of college education. Although bachelor's degree, master's degree, and doctoral degree are named categories, a strong argument can be made for considering them as strong ordinal data, since there is a progression from a bachelor's to a master's to doctorate. However, these same data could also reasonably be represented by the average number of years of schooling required to achieve the degree, or 16 years for a bachelor's degree, 18 years for a master's degree, and 22 years for a doctorate. This is a transformation to interval-level data with which few people would argue, and it may enhance the power of your data in techniques designed for multiple interval-level variables.

Most computer statistical programs, including the two we will use for examples, can do this kind of transformation quite easily. The two examples above and a number of other techniques that you may want to use to enhance the ability of your data to show true differences are known collectively as *data transformations.*

The appropriate use of most data-transformation techniques is more dependent on your knowledge of your subject and the meaning of the data you have collected than upon any specific mathematical or statistical techniques. You might well have another three-category variable that would not lend itself either to ordinal- or interval-level recoding, such as Ethnicity in which Black = 1, White = 2, and Other = 3. No one would argue that this is an ordinal-level variable; it could be recoded as interval only by creating two dummy variables. This transformation can be done, however, by using a simple recode, or "if(Ethnic = 1), then(Black = 1)," statement that can be found under RECODE or IF . . . THEN in the manual for the computer package available to you.

There are many more transformations available, but we will tell you only about two more that may be very useful to you, depending on your data. The first is for when you have a data set with a number of variables of greatly different metric, or size, range. Often this doesn't make a great deal of difference, but factor analysis, for example, is sometimes more likely to find importance in a variable such as income or program cost that ranges from $20,000 to $99,000 or $1 million to $20 million than in a zero-one variable, simply because of the math involved. If you suspect that this is so because of the results, you have two choices. The first, which is probably obvious, is to express the dollar variable in thousands or millions rather than dollars. If you have entered all the zeroes, just divide the variable by the appropriate amount before doing the analysis. This can be done on SPSS-X by using a COMPUTE command, or on SAS by entering NEWVARIABLE = OLDVARIABLE/1000. In the case of income, this would be something like INCOME = INCOME/1000, which would divide your income of $22,000 and make it a simple 22, a much smaller scale variable, which maintains the same relationship with all other values in the variable because all have been divided by the same amount. Therefore the variance among cases also remains the same and you have changed nothing in the relationship.

Another way to make sure that the scale of the variable is not causing difficulties in your analysis is to standardize the values on each variable. This assumes that those values are, or can be treated as, interval. In SPSS-X, use of the procedure command CONDESCRIPTIVE and Option 3 will convert all variables you select into Z-scores, standardized to a mean of 0 and a standard deviation of 1. The use of PROC STANDARD in SAS will produce the same result. This can be done in the same program in which you do your further analysis and the resulting standard scores can be used in the analysis. If this is difficult to believe, try it on a data set in which you are fairly sure you have no problems of scale. The new values will produce the same results as using the raw scores, but they may save you if you have real scale problems.

6.5 Treatment of Missing Data

Our last point about preparing your data is about the treatment of missing values. Since multivariate techniques use the matrix of all variables as the basis for any computation, they have to develop some rule as to what to do when a case has no value on some variable.

The most common decision, or *default,* what the program will do if you don't give it other commands, is called *listwise deletion.* This means that if there is one missing value, the whole case is omitted from the analysis. Most times, you can override the default when you give the procedure command, but you need to look at your data and think about what makes sense from what you know about your study.

Another common alternative is *pairwise deletion.* This means that the procedure will compute the correlation matrix, which is the basis for multiple regression or factor analysis, by computing the correlations between each pair of variables and will omit the case only from the correlation of that particular variable with each of the others. This means that all the information that you have will be used, but that some correlations will be only on those cases with non-missing values.

Neither deletion option is a problem if you have only one or two missing values on one or two cases. If there is a fair amount of missing data, however, you are going to have to think about its effects on your analysis. If you have only 50 cases, and 10 of those people refused to answer your question about income, you have two problems. First, if you allow the default listwise deletion to stand, you have only 40 cases to use in your analysis, and each of the 10 missing cases may have answered ten or twenty other questions. Since they are deleted from the analysis by the default deletion procedure, you lose all the other information they gave you. If your study is on the relationship between political preferences and income, you may need to leave the cases with missing income out, since income is crucial to testing your hypothesis. If your study is on the relationship between height, weight, and age, however, and you just asked income because it might possibly be related, you might select pairwise deletion on the grounds that the effect of income is secondary and you can just look at it in those cases when people gave it.

The other problem of missing data might be where you have a number of missing answers on a long questionnaire or series of measures, but the missing data are scattered, with one person not answering age, another not answering income, a third not giving political affiliation, a fourth not completing a depression scale, and so forth. If, on examining the data, the pattern of missing data looks random, you might consider substituting the mean value of each variable across all cases wherever that variable is missing. This involves specifying MISSING = MEANSUB on SPSS-X and PROC STANDARD REPLACE on SAS; either one will substitute the mean value of the named variable or series of variables across all cases for missing values. It has the advantage of letting you use all the information you have and all the cases, although you do not know if those who left those questions blank would have given the average or mean answer.

If your data have many missing answers to certain specific questions, you may want to omit those questions from your analysis or do a separate analysis on what you do know about them to see if they differ in any systematic way on the information you have from the people who answered those questions. If they do, omit them from your multiple variable analysis. If they don't, decide whether it makes sense to substitute the mean or average answer on those questions on which they are missing.

6.6 Choosing Which Test to Use

There is a series of questions to ask yourself in order to choose the appropriate statistical test. For those we are discussing here—five different tests that can be used to examine relationships between more than two characteristics—we will present an introductory overview of the information you will need to make that choice. More detailed information is available on each of these tests in the references noted in the appropriate chapters.

6.6.1 How Many Cases Do You Have?

If you have fewer than 100 or so cases and 30 or more variables, the only technique in this section that you can use with impunity is analysis of variance, and even that depends on having a relatively balanced design. That is, that each of the categories of your classification, criterion, or dependent variable must contain roughly the same number of cases.

If you can keep the number of variables of interest legitimately down to 10 or 15, then 60 or 70 cases will be enough to try any technique other than loglinear analysis, according to the more lenient rule of 50 more cases than variables. For loglinear analysis you will have to look at the distribution of your values (see Chapter 11). The important thing to remember is that, because of the nature of the calculations, you must consider the cases-to-variables correspondence. With too few cases, you reduce the power of the test to discern real relationships or significance. In other words, your results will be misleading and probably invalid.

6.6.2 What Is the Level of Measurement of Your Data?

If all of your variables are nominal, the only one of these techniques to use is log-linear analysis. If your dependent, criterion, or classification variable is nominal and the others are interval, dichotomous nominal, or strong ordinal, you may use analysis of variance or discriminant function analysis, but you may not use multiple regression. In this case, analysis of variance will tell you if your groups are different. Discriminant function analysis will tell you the relative importance of your variables in distinguishing

TABLE 6.1 Measurement Levels for Multivariate Techniques

Independent Variable(s)	Dependent Variable(s)	Statistic
Interval	Interval	Multiple Regression (Chapter 7)
Nominal	Interval	Analysis of Variance (Chapter 8)
Interval	Nominal	Discriminant Function (Chapter 10)
Nominal	Nominal	Log Linear Analysis (Chapter 11)

NOTE: It is not logical to think in terms of independent and dependent variables for factor analysis (Chapter 9). All data should be interval level or strong enough to be treated as interval level.

among groups and will classify cases using that information. Because multiple regression is based on the assumption of some linear relationship between the dependent or criterion variable and the set of independent or predictor variables, it is not appropriate to use it with nominal dependent variables. Factor analysis does not have dependent or criterion variables and may use a data set containing nominal dichotomous or ordinal variables if the majority of the variables are interval. Although levels of measurement are not the only criteria for choosing a multivariate technique, Table 6.1 can be used as a guide.

6.6.3 What Questions Are You Trying to Answer?

If you are looking for differences among several groups, *analysis of variance* will test that for you.

If you are looking for the relative individual and cumulative strength of the influence of a number of variables on another specific one, *multiple regression* will be a good choice.

If you are trying to find out which specific variables occur together in a certain pattern without reference to causality, to test if that pattern holds true in another data set, or to reduce the number of variables necessary to use in further analyses, factor analysis would be your choice.

If you want to develop a model from what you know about a population to be studied that would predict what you need to know for planning admissions based on nominal data, you would use *loglinear* or another kind of cross-classification analysis. If this were your choice and you also wanted to include one or two ordinal- or interval-level variables, you would collapse those variables into nominal categories, such as Under 21 and 21 and Over for age.

If you have clear nominal categories for a criterion or classification variable and want to know the relative importance of a number of other variables in predicting that classification, you would use *discriminant function analysis*.

If, as in most cases, you have more than one of the questions to answer, you may of course use more than one technique. Just as your data analysis began with frequencies, crosstabulations, and data clean-up, it can continue with a factor analysis in which you instruct the computer to build a data set with the factor scores as output and use them in further analysis, or move from one multivariate technique to another. For more detailed information than we can offer in this introductory overview, read any of the references in the appropriate chapter. General references on multivariate analysis that we have found to be helpful are Kerlinger (1973) and Kendall (1975).

CHAPTER 7

Multiple Regression Analysis

In the wrong hands, multiple regression analysis (MRA) can turn into Frankenstein's monster. However, with a little knowledge and the adherence to several basic principles, you can open up a whole new statistical world for yourself.

We think of multiple regression analysis as an explanatory technique rather than an exploratory technique. Unlike factor analysis, for example, where one needs to know very little about the bivariate relationships within the data, the use of multiple regression analysis requires a good sense of which ones are the important interval-level variables and how they might be related. Otherwise, you waste time and eat up a lot of computer processing units.

7.1 Introduction and Purpose

Essentially, regression analysis is the measurement ability of one or several independent or predictor variables to predict the values of one dependent or criterion variable. Why the technique is called "regression" seems lost in the Ice Age, but it has to do with bidirectional, mutual dependence whereby variables are said to "regress" upon one another.

There is both simple regression and multiple regression. In *simple regression,* one predictor variable is measured for its effect on one criterion variable. The outcome

107

is logically, if not mathematically, the same as bivariate correlational analysis. In multiple regression analysis, several predictor variables are measured for the effect on one criterion variable. More about this concept later.

You may have noticed we made a switch in terminology from using independent and dependent variables to predictor and criterion variables. We were using the term *independent variable* to describe characteristics that logically might influence, even cause, variation in a *dependent variable*. Here we want to be more specific. Because all the variables we want to correlate were probably chosen randomly, we really cannot know if the relationships are causal. However, we can measure how much the values in one characteristic predict values in another, whether that relationship is causal, apparent, or confounding. Therefore, we use the more precise term *predictor variable*.

In most studies, some variables are obviously more important than others. For example, in a study of the effects of budget cuts on the income of public aid recipients, the variable Income is all-important. In a study of client longevity in counseling, the number of client appointments is all-important. These essential (logically speaking) dependent variables are the *criterion variables*.

The purpose, therefore, of multiple regression analysis is to measure the relative importance of several predictor variables on one criterion variable. Let us begin with an example of what this might mean before going on to more technical material. Suppose you work in a mental health clinic and want to test the effect of group treatment on the social functioning of clients. A standardized test of social functioning is used to measure outcome. You determine that (1) the number of group sessions attended is correlated positively with outcome and that (2) the number of individual psychotherapy sessions also correlates positively with outcome. How much of the change in social functioning is predicted by attendance in group therapy and in individual therapy? If the effects of attendance in both treatments are *combined,* how much do they predict? If they both predict change in social functioning, what are the *relative* effects of each? In other words, which variable is more important and by how much? These are the kinds of questions multiple regression analysis can answer.

7.2 The Linear Equation

The simplest relationship between two variables is a straight line. Such a relationship between a predictor variable X and a criterion variable Y can be expressed as the following formula:

$$Y = a + bX$$

The coefficient *a* is the intercept or *constant,* that is, the point on the X axis where Y intercepts. Technically, the *constant* is the value of Y when X is zero. The coefficient *b* is the *slope,* that is, the change in Y accounted for by a one-unit change in X.

For a simple example, we can look at how gross income is correlated with base pay plus commissions. Suppose a car salesman earns $10,000 per year in salary plus $200 for every car he sells. His gross annual income (Y) would equal $10,000 (the constant, or coefficient *a*) plus $200 (the coefficient *b*) times the number of cars he sold (X). Y intercepts X at $10,000 and goes up $200 for every car sold, that is, for every unit of X. If the salesman sells 10 cars in one year, he earns $12,000. Once the value of X is known (the number of cars sold), the value of Y (annual income) is known. This perfect linear relationship is shown in Figure 7.1.

Perfect linear relationships are probably nonexistent in the human services. However, for the moment let us consider some hypothetically perfect data. Table 7.1 repre-

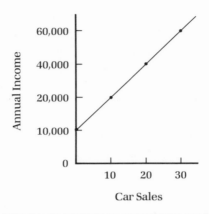

FIGURE 7.1 Perfect Linear Relationship

sents the relationship between change in social functioning and attendance at group therapy.

Just by eyeballing the data, we can see that there is a positive relationship between attendance and higher scores on a social functioning scale. In fact, the relationship is even more exact. Everyone scored on change in social functioning at least three plus two times the number of therapy sessions. In other words, the formula $Y = a + bX$ in this case is $Y = 3 + 2X$. The constant equals 3. Everyone scored at least three on change in social functioning. The total score was determined by adding twice the

TABLE 7.1 Improvement in Social Functioning and Group Attendance

Participant	Change in Social Functioning (Y)	Number of Sessions Attended (X)
A	15	6
B	17	7
C	13	5
D	21	9

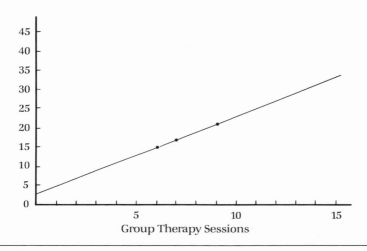

FIGURE 7.2 Linear Equation Y = 3 + 2X for the Relationship Between Group Attendance and Social Functioning

number of sessions attended. Graphically, this relationship is represented in Figure 7.2.

The example is simplistic, but it illustrates an important aspect of the power of multiple regression analysis. If you know the value of X, you can *predict* the value of Y. If you know how many group therapy sessions were attended, you can predict the level of social functioning.

7.3 The Principle of Least Squares

The *regression line* is an imaginary line running through various *scatterplots* or visual representations where each dot, or data point, represents one case with a corresponding value of X and Y. The regression line is the linear equivalent of the mean or, more precisely, the average predicted score for any value of X. The technique for determining the exact location of the regression line, that is,

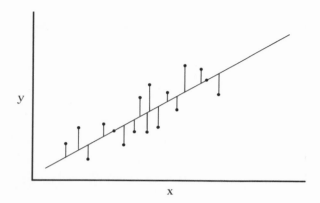

FIGURE 7.3 The Principle of Least Squares

its slope and Y intercept, is called the *least squares method.* See Figure 7.3 and note the distances between each data point and the regression line. Of all the lines that are possible, the one with the smallest sum of squared distances from each data point to the line is selected. This process is called "looking for the best fit."

The shortest distance from any data point to the regression line is called a *residual.* Each residual represents error, namely, the difference between the actual value of Y and its predicted value.

So the regression line has to do with prediction. For any known value of the predictor variable X, the unknown Y value is assumed to be found on the regression line at the point corresponding to the value of X.

7.4 Assumptions

Like other statistics, multiple regression analysis is appropriate when certain assumptions about the nature of the data to be used are met. If the assumptions cannot be met to some reasonable degree, then (1) the results cannot be used to generalize about the population from which the sample was drawn, and/or (2) the procedure may not be appropriate. In this section we will identify those assumptions, how to test for compliance, and what to do when the assumptions are violated. When a point gets too technical for our purposes, we will refer you to more advanced sources.

For those of you who are using this material as an introduction, we have to remind you that statistics is not an exact science. There is plenty of room for opinion and controversy. If you look at several texts on multiple regression analysis, the various treatments on the subject of assumptions might not resemble one another at all, because there are different opinions about how important things are. What we are presenting here is what *we* think is correct, important, and useful.

In multiple regression analysis, like other inferential statistics, there are essentially two points of view regarding assumptions: the "robust" view and the "fragile" view. Those who take the *robust view* hold that the validity of the results derived from multiple regression analysis will not be unduly influenced by violating the assumptions (Kerlinger and Pedhazur, 1973). Others, who take the fragile view, think that violating assumptions renders the results useless (Bibby, 1977). We tend to side with the robust point of view as long as the whole process remains rational. We'll explain further as we go along.

7.4.1 Interval-Level Data

Interval-level data or data that can reasonably be treated as interval level is required for multiple regression analysis. See Chapter 1 for a more complete explanation of levels of measurement.

7.4.2 Linearity

MRA is based on an assumption of *linearity,* which means
that the relationship between the criterion variable and
the predictor variable can be expressed, more or less, in
terms of a straight line. Simply put, Variable A increases
as Variable B increases, Variable A decreases as Variable B
decreases, or Variable A increases as Variable B decreases
fairly consistently and without a lot of oddball cases. It is
possible for such relationships to be statistically significant, but not linear. See our section in Chapter 4 on nonparametric correlation, for example.

If the relationship is not linear, it is probably either
nonexistent or curvilinear. See Figure 7.4 for scatterplots
of linear, nonexistent, and curvilinear relationships.

If the relationship is linear, the data will tend to accu-
mulate along an imaginary straight line running through
the scatterpoints. There will be few oddball cases, referred to as *outliers.* Examples of outliers would include a
man who, no matter how many group treatment sessions
he attended, never improved, or a woman who improved
dramatically in social functioning after only the first meet-
ing. Outliers constitute a major consideration in the use of
MRA, and their treatment will be dealt with throughout
this chapter.

If there is no relationship, then the scatterplot should
look like randomly placed dots. However, the scatterplot
can look like a large pepperoni pizza and still be linear.
For instance, the scatterplot could be distorted because it
is out of proportion to the values of the data. This can be
determined by using one of a number of techniques discussed in more advanced texts. Tests for linearity discussed below are also useful.

Recall that we said the relationship between group
therapy and social functioning was, for the purpose of illustration, hypothetically linear. In reality, such relationships are usually curvilinear, meaning that the increase/

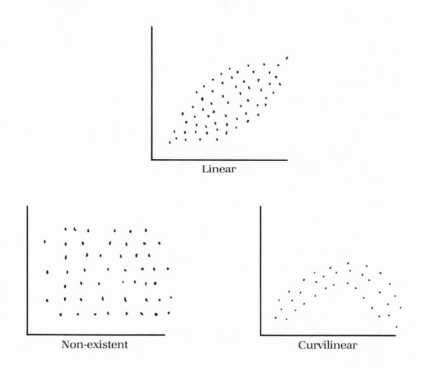

Linear

Non-existent

Curvilinear

FIGURE 7.4 Linear, Nonexistent, and Curvilinear Relationships

increase, decrease/decrease, increase/decrease configuration does not remain constant for all values of the predictor variable. When dealing with human subjects, such inconsistency makes perfect sense. Attending one or two group therapy sessions may not benefit anyone. On the other hand, a point of diminishing returns will also be reached. The participants cannot go on indefinitely improving.

So how do you test for linearity? There are two good methods. The first entails simply inspecting the scatterplots. The second entails using the procedure BREAK-DOWN in SPSS-X. The output includes significance tests for linearity, departure from linearity, and the statistic *eta*. Eta is a measure of curvilinear relationship. (Eta squared is the curvilinear equivalent of r^2, which will be discussed shortly.) Let's establish a general, reasonable rule of thumb. The relationship is linear if it obviously looks linear or if, according to the BREAKDOWN procedure, (1) the relationship is linear at P < .05 *or* (2) the relationship does not depart from linearity at P < .05 *and* eta squared is not greater than .25.

What if the relationship is not linear? It depends on what is causing the problem. If the outliers are extreme, the regression line teeters, making accurate prediction of the Y values difficult. You could do one or more of the following:

- exclude the outliers and report two equations, one with and one without the outliers;
- if possible, gather more data and hope the outliers are not as anomalous as they looked with the smaller sample; or
- transform the variable using weighted least squares.

The weighted least squares procedure scrunches the data and flattens it out along the regression line.[1] One disadvantage is that, along with the residuals, the output is transformed too. So significance can be reported, the relationship may be linear, but the numbers may be difficult to interpret.

If the relationships are curvilinear, use the scatterplots to interpret the data and test for an eta squared greater than .25.

---

[1]The procedure is not available in SPSS-X or SAS, but there are ways to mock it. You will need a consultant on this one.

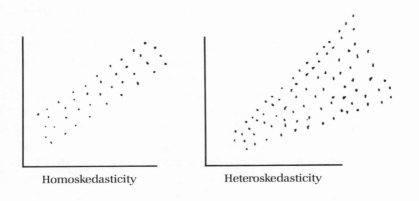

Homoskedasticity   Heteroskedasticity

FIGURE 7.5 Homoskedasticity and Heteroskedasticity

7.4.3 Homoskedasticity

MRA is based on an assumption of *homoskedasticity,* which means consistent variance. Figure 7.5 contains both examples of homoskedasticity and its violation, heteroskedasticity. In the condition of homoskedasticity, the data points lie on either side of the imaginary regression line consistently and independently of the values of X.

Consider, for a moment, three subgroups of our subjects receiving group treatment: those who attend a few sessions and improve a little, those who attend a moderate number and improve moderately, and those who attend many sessions and improve substantially. Homoskedasticity means that the range of improvement for each of the subgroups will be approximately the same.

Heteroskedasticity means that the ranges are not the same, that the variance increases or decreases with increasing values of X. In Figure 7.5 the variance increases in the illustration to the right. As the number of sessions attended increases, the differences in social functioning expand. For some reason, those who received the most treatment either improved the most or regressed the most. Such a violation of the assumption of homoskedasticity can result in the distortion of confidence levels and significance testing, that is, spurious findings.

The problem is that, when dealing with human subjects, one can expect such differences whenever the variables under study entail any measurement of growth, learning, or development. Individuals simply do not grow or learn at the same rates, even when afforded the same opportunities and experiences. Therefore, in our opinion, a certain amount of inconsistent variance must be tolerated in human services research.

For the detection of homoskedasticity, you will need to rely on eyeballing the scatterplots and hope they don't look like ice cream cones lying on their sides, like the righthand scatterplot in Figure 7.5. If they do, you could eliminate those values of X causing the problem, simply report the phenomenon as a finding, or employ the variable transformation with weighted least squares.

7.4.4 Error and the Independent Variable

The assumption is that the independent or predictor variable does not correlate with error. Simply put, this means that it is assumed that something very important has not been left out. In nonexperimental research, where we have no control over the independent variables, this assumption is almost impossible to meet.

Suppose that the number of individual sessions in psychotherapy accounts for almost as much change in social functioning as the group sessions, but we do not know the number of individual sessions per subject. This important missing information, or error, may correlate with the number of group sessions, and both may affect outcome.

If you use multiple regression analysis and the results are significant but weak, there may be an error in the predictor variable, or you may not have included all important predictor variables. The solution is to plug more information into the process or, if unavailable, to plan better next time.

7.4.5 Normal Distribution

There may be a more technical or more complicated way of saying this, but essentially, it is assumed that all the variables in the multiple regression analysis procedure are normally distributed. All the values of each variable should conform to the bell-shaped curve, with the mean, median, and mode equal and 95% of the observations lying within two standard deviation units, plus or minus, from the mean.

In order to test for normality you can graph the distributions and eyeball the shapes, check to see if about half the observations fall on either side of the mean, or use a statistic that measures skewness or deviation from the normal curve. You can obtain a measure of skewness with the FREQUENCIES procedure on SPSS-X. Perfect skewness equals 0.

Of all the assumptions, normal distribution is probably the most robust, that is, the one you can fudge on the most, especially if you have at least 100 cases.

7.5 The Concept of Explained Variance

Regression analysis is essentially a measure of *explained variance,* the extent which, expressed as a percentage, the difference in values of one variable, or a combination of variables, explains, determines, or accounts for the difference in values of another variable. By using multiple regression analysis, we can determine, for example, how much variance in attending group therapy sessions accounts for the variance in social functioning. In multiple regression analysis we want to determine the effect of a combination of predictor variables and their relative strengths. Thus, multiple regression analysis is used to determine how much group treatment and individual psychotherapy predict change in social functioning and in what order.

When a relationship is essentially linear but weak, there is a fair amount of unexplained variance present. Unexplained variance can result from the omission of important predictor variables and/or measurement error.

7.6 Ordering of the Predictor Variables

Ordering the predictor variables is very important to MRA. Although there are many ways to treat variable inclusion, hierarchical inclusion and stepwise inclusion are the most common.

In hierarchical hypotheses, one assumes that one group of predictor variables is more important than another group. For example, one might hypothesize that, although both are important, the number of group psychotherapy sessions contributes to social functioning more than the number of individual sessions. That particular relationship is then tested for a significant "fit" on the regression line.

The stepwise procedure is more exploratory. The computer includes and excludes the predictor variables as more and more of the variance in the criterion variable is explained until a point of diminishing returns is reached. You can assume that when we talk about MRA, we mean the stepwise procedure, if there is not a strong theoretical basis to determine a hierarchical inclusion.

7.7 Output Statistics

There are several necessary and useful output statistics that result from the multiple regression analysis procedure. They include the multiple R, the R^2, the adjusted R^2, the b coefficients, the Beta weights, and the F test for significance of the slope. For purposes of illustration, we are going to continue with our example of the relationship between standardized scores on social functioning and number of group therapy sessions attended. We are also going to add (1) six cases so we have an N of 10 and (2) a second variable: the number of individual psychotherapy sessions attended. The task will be to interpret the relative strengths of group and individual treatment on social functioning. Recall our basic formula for a straight line:

$$Y = a + bX.$$

In multiple regression analysis, the formula becomes

$$Y = a + b(X_1) + b(X_2) \ldots + b(X_N).$$

In our example, this means to us that

social functioning = constant + b (number of group sessions) + b (number of individual sessions).

Using our output statistics, we will determine the values for these symbolic representations and interpret their meaning. The raw data is found in Table 7.2.

7.7.1 Multiple R and R^2

In our section on correlation in Chapter 4, we said that the statistic for the linear relationship of two interval-level variables was Pearson's r. We did not say then, but it is crucial now, that R^2 is a measurement of explained vari-

TABLE 7.2 Sample Raw Data

Subject	Value on Social Functioning (Y)	Number of Group Sessions (X_1)	Number of Individual Sessions (X_2)
A	15	6	13
B	17	7	13
C	13	5	12
D	21	9	16
E	21	10	21
F	22	8	16
G	23	12	21
H	14	4	10
I	15	7	14
J	13	4	8

ance.[2] By squaring R, the extent of variance in one variable or characteristic accounted for by another is determined. The R^2 is expressed as a percentage so it is easily interpreted.

In multiple regression analysis, the multiple R is the measure of correlation between the criterion variable and the multiple predictor variables. Actually, it is also the measurement of correlation between two variables *where the independent or predictor variable is a combination of the multiple predictor variables weighted for their relative importance.* In our example, multiple R is the correlation between the criterion variable (social functioning) and the predictor variables (group sessions plus individual sessions).

By extension, the multiple r^2 is a measure of explained variance, expressed as a percentage, between the criterion variable and the derived predictor variable (group sessions and individual sessions). Because some of the variation in the R^2 statistic is expected by chance, especially

---

[2]Technically, it is the ratio of the variance in one variable to the variance in the other.

TABLE 7.3 Output Statistics for Multiple Regression Analysis: Social Functioning by Group Therapy and Individual Psychotherapy

$R = .92$ $R^2 = .84$ $F = 18.32$ $P < .002$

	b coefficient	beta	F	Probability
Intercept (constant)	7.61			
Group Therapy	1.47	.92	3.09	$P < .13$
Individual Psychotherapy	– .01	– .01	.01	$P < .9$

when the number of cases is small, sometimes the R^2 is adjusted downward to compensate for that effect. Output from SPSS-X includes the adjusted R^2 squared. SAS does not.

When the data from Table 7.2 is run on the computer, the R is equal to .92 and the R^2 is equal to .84 (or a program evaluator's dream). All the output statistics are found in Table 7.3.

The table indicates that the number of group therapy and individual sessions strongly predict scores on social functioning. The greater the number of sessions, the better the functioning. Combined, they predict or account for 94% of the variance in social functioning, a very strong relationship. Any R^2 greater than .25 is worth reporting. An R^2 of .92 is both strong and statistically significant. It means that the predictor variable derived from combination of individual and group sessions accounts for all but 16% of the variance in social functioning.

7.7.2 Beta Weights and Coefficients

According to the output in Table 7.3, the number of group therapy sessions and the number of individual psychotherapy sessions are not equal in their predictive ability. The coefficient for group therapy is much higher. Although it is not actually meaningless, the number of individual sessions appears meaningless. The R^2 for social functioning and group sessions is the same as R^2 for social functioning and group sessions plus individual sessions unless the R^2 is carried out to more than three places. One might use that finding to support the argument that only group therapy is important because, unlike individual psychotherapy, group therapy is a "social" experience and our interest is in measuring social functioning. However, such an interpretation is spurious. We will explain why shortly.

But first, let's look at the constant, the b coefficients, and the betas in Table 7.3. As we said before, the constant or Y intercept is the value of Y when X is zero. So with no therapy whatsoever, in our example all the subjects would score at least 7.61 on social functioning.

The b coefficients are the slopes, the amount of change in Y for every unit change in X. They are used in predicting actual values in the multiple regression analysis equation. For every one group therapy session, the social functioning score increases by 1.47 and for every individual treatment session, the effect on social functioning is nil (–.01).

Let's test this model by plugging in some raw data from Table 7.2. We will use the information from Subject B. For the model

social functioning = constant + b (Number of group sessions) + b (Number of individual sessions),

we get the calculations in Figure 7.6.

So Subject B, who had 7 group therapy sessions and 13 individual sessions, is expected to score 17.77 on social functioning. In fact, he scored 17. The discrepancy of .77 is due to error, i.e. departure from linearity.

The *beta weights* are not as readily interpreted. They represent transformations of the b coefficients into standardized z-scores. They are, however, *used in assessing*

social functioning = constant + b (N of group sessions)
                     + b (N of individual sessions)

or

social functioning = 7.61 + 1.47(7) + (– .01) (13)

or

social functioning = 7.61 + 10.29 + (– .13)

or

social functioning = 17.77

FIGURE 7.6 Predicted Social Functioning Score for Subject B

the relative importance of each predictor variable to the derived predictor variable. In this case, number of group therapy sessions, with a beta of .92, overwhelms number of individual sessions with a beta of –.01. However, there is a fly in the statistical ointment. The first clue to the problem is found in the significance tests.

7.7.3 Significance Tests of the Slope

Multiple regression analysis is a test for the strength and magnitude of a linear relationship. The R^2 statistic is a measure of that relationship. However, the R^2 is not a test of significance, so the F *ratio* is employed to test whether or not the R^2 could have been achieved by chance. Technically speaking, if no relationship exists between the criterion variable and the predictor variables, there would be no slope. The null hypothesis, therefore, is that the slope equals zero, or

$$H_0: b = 0.$$

The F test then measures the probability of the demonstrated relationship representing a chance departure from a straight line. More about the F test in Chapter 8.

As seen in table 7.3, $F = 18.32$ for the entire model, with the probability of achieving such a result by chance being 2 in 1,000. In the hypothetical example, very strong evidence exists that group therapy and individual psychotherapy predict or account for a great deal of the variance in social functioning.

The output statistics also include an F ratio for testing the effect of plugging each variable into the regression equation one at a time, or stepwise. For the example in Table 7.3, the second predictor variable, individual psychotherapy, has caused the first predictor variable, group therapy, to be nonsignificant. Whereas $F = 18.32$, $P < .002$, for the entire model, group therapy drops to $F = 3.09$, $P < .13$, when individual psychotherapy is entered into the equation. This is strong evidence that something is gumming up the works, and that something is likely to be multicollinearity.

7.8 Multicollinearity

Multicollinearity is simply very high correlation between the predictor variables. Such a condition adversely affects the variances within the mathematical computations that are used for multiple regression analysis, distorting the results. Unfortunately, multicollinearity is commonplace in nonexperimental research typical of the human services. For example, think of the variables age, income, socioeconomic class, and education. Although the relationships between these commonly measured characteristics are not perfectly linear, within certain populations they will intercorrelate very highly.

In the example we have been using to explain multiple regression analysis, multicollinearity between the two

TABLE 7.4 Regression R^2 for All Variables

Criterion Variable	Predictor Variable	R^2	Probability
Social Functioning	Group Therapy	.84	P < .001
Social Functioning	Individual Therapy	.77	P < .001
Group Therapy	Individual Therapy	.93	P < .001

predictor variables—Number of Group Therapy Sessions and Number of Individual Psychotherapy Sessions—is present. The result is to make invisible the effect of individual therapy on social functioning. According to Table 7.3, only group therapy can predict the social functioning scores, but look at Table 7.4 and see what happens when all the variables are regressed against one another.

Separately, both group therapy and individual psychotherapy predict social functioning, while at the same time, the relationship between number of group sessions and individual sessions is even stronger.

There are several ways of detecting the presence of multicollinearity. Originally, we found in our example that the regression equation was statistically significant, but when subsequent variables were entered into the model, the F ratios for each step were not significant. That was our first clue. Running a correlation matrix and looking for very high Pearson's r coefficients can be helpful too, but the best method is the one we used in Table 7.4: regressing the predictor variables against one another and looking for an R^2 greater than .90.

Once the problem of multicollinearity is diagnosed, there are two things that can be done about it. First, we can drop the problematical variables from the equation and report the results separately. This is unfortunate, but it may be the only possibility if the second solution isn't viable.

The second solution is to combine the multi-correlated predictor variables *if logically possible and, therefore, interpretable.* In our case it is. We could transform the variables by adding the number of group sessions to the number of individual sessions and create the variable Number of Therapeutic Sessions. In our example, the result would be $R^2 = .81$, $F = 34.1$, $P < .001$. We could then say with some authority that a combination of group and individual therapy predicts improved social functioning. Obviously, such a solution would not be possible if the predictor variables were not logically related. For example, it would not make sense to add the number of group therapy sessions to the subject's income.

7.9 Set-Up Requirements

So far we have tried to explain the uses of multiple regression analysis and how to interpret the results. We will end this chapter by going over the data requirements for the procedure.

7.9.1 Number of Variables and Level of Measurement

Although only two variables are needed for simple regression, the more interesting stepwise procedure requires one criterion variable and at least two predictor variables, all of which should be interval or ratio level.

7.9.2 Criterion and Predictor Variables

It is important that the criterion variable be logically dependent. One could test how well social functioning predicts attendance in therapy, but unless one is studying factors that contribute to client continuation in treatment, it does not make sense to do so.

7.9.3 *N* of Cases

There were ten cases used in the example for this chapter, but ordinarily this would not be sufficient for multiple regression analysis. We mentioned in an earlier chapter that 30 cases are needed for statistical stability. This is a good rule of thumb for bivariate statistics, but for multivariates there should be ideally ten cases for every variable in the procedure, or at least 50 more cases than the number of variables if you have only 10 or 15 variables (see Chapter 6).

Worrying about the assumptions that underlie the multiple regression analysis procedure can be significantly reduced when the N is greater than 100. However, when there are too many cases, say, more than 1,000, even the weakest relationships can appear significant. In that circumstance, we suggest taking a random sample of your sample in order to reduce your *N.* Use the procedure SAMPLE in SPSS-X.

7.9.4 Dummy Variables

The robust view contends that dichotomous or dummy predictor variables hold up rather well in the multiple regression analysis procedure. We agree with that view up to a point. Because adding more and more predictor variables to the equation increases the degrees of freedom, we caution against creating too many variables from one nominal-level characteristic. For example, if you take the variable Religion and create five or six dummy variables, such as Protestant/Not Protestant or Catholic/Not Catholic, and then plug all of them into a regression procedure, you are stacking the deck in favor of religion as a predictor. Use two or three dummy variables from one nominal characteristic at most.

SAS

PROC STEPWISE:
  MODEL SOCIAL = GROUP PSYCHO/MAXR;

SPSS-X

REGRESSION VARIABLES = SOCIAL GROUP PSYCHO/
  DEPENDENT = SOCIAL/STEPWISE

FIGURE 7.7 Sample Regression Procedures from SAS and SPSS-X

The use of dummy variables as criterion variables is more fragile. For example, suppose the criterion variable is Employment with values of (0) Not Employed and (1) Employed. The procedure is supposed to explain variance, but there is no variance between Not Employed and Employed. You either have a job or you do not. You are left with the interpretation that the predictor variables account for a "tendency" to be employed or not. You are better off not using this kind of dummy variable as a criterion variable.

7.9.5 Size of Variance

If there is too little variance in a predictor variable X, the relationship could be linear and, significant, but it might not show up in the output statistics. Should the scatterplot indicate such a problem, check the standard deviation of that characteristic to make sure. If the problem exists, the only solution is to gather more extreme values of X.

7.10 Sample Multiple Regression Stepwise Procedures

The examples of multiple regression analysis used in this chapter were derived from the SAS and SPSS-X procedures seen in Figure 7.7.

CHAPTER 8

Analysis of Variance

This chapter is about multiple independent or predictor variables at the nominal level of measurement and one dependent or criterion variable at the interval level of measurement. In contrast to multiple regression analysis, whereby one seeks the best "fit" among the variables, analysis of variance (ANOVA) determines whether the discrete categories within a nominal-level predictor variable discriminate among high or low values in the dependent variable. The nominal-level independent variables are also referred to as *factors* (which some authors call explanatory variables).

ANOVA is both fascinating and, at times, frustrating (more about the frustrating part later). We are going to begin with an example using one factor containing three categories, then two factors, and then two factors with a covariate. This should give you a pretty good idea of how to use this procedure, although the discussion will be far from exhaustive.

8.1 Assumptions and Set-Up Requirements

Statistics have a life of their own and, because they are derived from mathematics, results can be spurious unless certain rules are followed. At least with ANOVA, we do not have to be concerned about linearity, a crucial requirement for multiple regression analysis.

8.1.1 Level of Measurement

Interval-level of measurement is required for the dependent variable. It is not appropriate to use dichotomous dummy variables for the dependent or criterion variable. Discriminant function analysis can be used when the dependent variable is categorical. One can collapse interval-level data into categories for use as predictor variables in ANOVA, but some power in the analysis will be lost.

8.1.2 Number of Cases

One should have at least ten cases for every variable in the procedure. For ANOVA, it is also important that the predictor categories contain roughly the same number of cases.

8.1.3 Multicollinearity

It is important that the predictor variables not be dependent on one another. When they are, it is not possible to disentangle their unique effects on the dependent variable. The relationship between the predictor variables can be tested using the chi-square test for statistical independence. If they are not independent of each other, you have a problem.

8.1.4 Fixed Versus Random Models

Our discussion of ANOVA will be limited to what is called a *fixed model* as opposed to a *random model*. By fixed model, we mean that our intent is not to generalize any results beyond the subjects under study. In a random model, the predictor categories are selected randomly from a larger population of categories and, therefore, are presumed to represent categories not in the analysis.

8.1.5 Normal Distribution

Like all parametric statistics, ANOVA requires that the observations in the dependent variable be selected randomly from a theoretically normal distribution of values. Although ANOVA has been shown to be robust and moderate departures from normality can be tolerated, it is wise to chart the residuals using a histogram in order to determine whether the dependent variable is, at least roughly, randomly distributed. Recall from Chapter 7 that residuals are the individual distances from a value and its group mean. If there are too many extreme values in one category, those cases will have an unrealistic effect on the group variance, because the variance is derived from squared values.

8.1.6 Ordering of the Independent Variables

When there is more than one predictor variable, the order in which they are entered into the procedure can affect the outcome. In our subsequent example, ordering does not affect the outcome, but one should always check for this possibility. When ordering affects results, we recommend interpreting the model that is most highly significant.

8.2 ANOVA and the Output Statistics

In the following section, we will review the output that is generated by the ANOVA procedure and how to interpret it. To begin with, we will demonstrate *one-way analysis of variance*. This refers to measuring the effects of one factor with multiple categories on one interval-level dependent variable. Let's use an example, similar to one we used in Chapter 4, but with more information. We survey a number of teachers and collect data on their level of edu-

TABLE 8.1 Sample Data for ANOVA

Education	Gender	Income	Age
B.A.	Male	$16,000	37
M.A.	Female	22,000	43
Ph.D.	Male	26,000	47
B.A.	Female	16,000	37
M.A.	Male	20,000	41
Ph.D.	Female	21,000	42
B.A.	Male	13,000	34
M.A.	Female	21,000	42
Ph.D.	Male	30,000	51
B.A.	Female	14,000	35
M.A.	Male	20,000	41
Ph.D.	Female	22,000	43

cation, gender, income, and age. The raw data are found in Table 8.1.

In order to meet the requirement for sufficient number of cases and, at the same time, increase the degrees of freedom, all the data will be duplicated in our sample statistics so that $N = 48$ instead of $N = 12$. In our one-way ANOVA, we will hypothesize that different educational backgrounds result in statistically different incomes.

Before we go on, let's take a look at the cell means for the three categories of education in Table 8.2. Obviously, average income is very different for the three levels of education and, according to our first analysis, the results are highly significant. Although they will vary from one sta-

TABLE 8.2 Cell Means for Income by Level of Education

Level of Education	N	Mean Income
B.A.	16	$14,750
M.A.	16	20,750
Ph.D.	16	24,750

TABLE 8.3 ANOVA: Income by Level of Education

	Sum of Squares	DF	Mean Square	F	Significance
Main Effects	810	2	405	75.69	0.0
Education	810	2	405	75.69	0.0
Explained Variance	810	2	405	75.69	0.0
Residual	241	45	5		
Total	1051	47	22		

NOTE: The values under Sum of Squares and Mean Square are rounded and represent the actual value times 1,000,000. For example, the actual Sum of Squares for the Main Effects was 1,051,666,666.667 on SPSS-X.

tistical package to another, the results should look something like Table 8.3.

Let's now break down these results into their individual components.

8.2.1 Sum of Squares

The total *sum of squares* is the sum of the variation for all the subjects. It is the overall group mean of the dependent variable subtracted from every case, squared, and added together. (Now you can see how it can become such a large number.) It is useful and important to think of the total sum of squares as 100% of the variance.

In Chapter 7, we discussed explained and unexplained variance. Although we are not dealing with linear relationships like we were with multiple regression analysis, the concepts are still relevant to ANOVA. We are attempting to account for or explain the variance in the criterion variable that is attributable to the predictor variable—in Table 8.3, the Main Effects. Because there is only one predictor variable, Education, the Main Effects variation and the total explained variance are the same thing. *The residual (effects) are simply the unexplained variance,* in this case, the variation in income not accounted for by education. The explained variance plus the unexplained variance equals the total variance, that is, the main effects plus the residual effects equals the total sum of squares.

8.2.2 Degrees of Freedom

The total degrees of freedom for the entire model equals $N-1$ cases. The degrees of freedom for the various effects is equal to $N-1$ categories, or groups. The residual degrees of freedom equals N cases minus N groups.

8.2.3 Mean Square and the *F* Ratio

The *mean square* is equal to the sum of squares divided by the degrees of freedom, a way of taking into account or weighting the relative importance of the number of cases and categories.

The *F* ratio is determined by dividing the mean square of the Explained variance by the mean square of the residual. In other words, if we take it from the top, the greater the difference in means between categories, the greater the variation explained by the categories, the smaller the residual, the larger the *F*, and the greater the likelihood the differences do not result from chance. In our example, the chances of the differences being random are so small, the computer rounded off the probability to 0.0.

8.2.4 Eta Squared

You may recall that R^2 was the measure for explained variance, expressed as a percentage, for multiple regression analysis. *Eta squared* is the ANOVA equivalent. It is calculated by subtracting the residual sum of squares from the total sum of squares and dividing by the total sum of squares, a kind of ANOVA batting average. Like the R^2, eta squared is important because results can be weak (an eta squared less than .25), but the F can be significant. In our example the result is $(1051 - 241)/1051$ or .77, meaning 77% explained variance, a very strong finding.

Although eta squared is the only measure of the model's power, it is not part of the computer output. This is one of the frustrations of ANOVA.

8.3 Factorial Designs

In factorial designs, ANOVA measures the interaction effects of multiple predictor variables or factors. What do we mean by an interaction? We stated that ANOVA searches for differences in the high and low scores between categories. By *interaction*, we mean differences that result from crosstabulating predictor categories. In our example, we know that education determines differences in income. We also know by the *t*-test we ran in Chapter 4 that gender by itself does not. The mean income for all the men is $20,833.33 compared to $19,333.33 for the women— different, but not statistically significant. But could the interaction of education and gender make a difference? The cell means for this analysis are seen in Table 8.4.

This adds a new perspective, doesn't it? What we find is that gender is important in the context of education. It is the male Ph.D.'s who are making a disproportionately higher salary than the female Ph.D.'s. The findings are highly significant, as seen in Table 8.5.

Notice that the effects of education, gender, and the interaction of education and gender all make a difference and contribute to the explained variance. Notice too that the Explained Variance sum of squares is made up of the Main Effects sum of squares plus the Interactions sum of squares.

**TABLE 8.4 Cell Means for Income by Education and
Gender**

	Gender	
Education	*Male*	*Female*
B.A.	14,500	15,000
M.A.	20,000	21,500
Ph.D.	28,000	21,500

NOTE: N = 8 for each cell.

This may get a little confusing, but it is useful to compare the results in Table 8.5 with Table 8.3. In both tables,
the Main Effects sum of squares and the total sum of
squares are the same. It is possible, therefore, to measure
exactly the contribution of gender and the education/gen-

**TABLE 8.5 ANOVA: Income by Level of Education and
Gender**

	Sum of Squares	DF	Mean Square	F	Significance
Main Effects	837	3	279	189.15	0.0
Education	810	2	405	274.58	0.0
Gender	27	1	27	18.29	0.0
Interactions					
Education/Gender	152	2	76	51.48	0.0
Explained Variance	989	5	197	134.08	0.0
Residual	62	42	1		
Total	1051	47	22		

NOTE: The values under Sum of Squares and Mean Square are rounded and
represent the actual value times 1,000,000. For example, the actual Sum of
Squares for the Main Effects was 1,051,666,666.667 on SPSS-X.

der interaction to the total explained variance. Look again at Table 8.5. Some of you might ask, "Why is the main effect of gender significant when income by gender was not significant using a t-test?" First, the F-test is more sensitive to variation than the t-test. Secondly, we have to take into account the eta squared. Although the main effect of gender is significant, eta squared is equal to a mere .03. (We derived that figure by dividing gender's sum of squares by the total sum of squares (27/1051).) However, the interaction of education and gender results in an eta squared of .14 (152/1051), not overwhelming, but 14% explained variance is worth reporting.

We find ourselves with a powerful model here. Eta squared has been raised to .94. Notice that the eta squared of .94 in Table 8.5 minus the eta squared of .77 in Table 8.3 is equal to the contribution of gender (.17) as a main effect and an interaction.

8.4 Covariance

There is one more aspect to ANOVA that we want to demonstrate: the addition of an interval-level covariate to the above procedure. Suppose we know from our bivariate analysis that income correlates highly with age. (For the sake of explication, we fudged this. Income and age actually correlate perfectly.) We need to insert the variable Age into our analysis. There are now two predictor variables or factors, one (Education) has three categories and one (Gender) has two categories, with one criterion variable (Income), plus another interval-level variable, or covariate, (Age) that may or may not explain some of the variance in the criterion variable. In other words, we want to test the effects of education and gender on income taking into account the age of the subjects. Let's look at the cell means in Table 8.6.

TABLE 8.6 Cell Means for Age by Education and Gender

	Age	
Education	Male	Female
B.A.	35.5	36
M.A.	41	42.5
Ph.D.	49	42.5

NOTE: N = 8 for each cell.

The male Ph.D.'s make more money than anyone else, but they are also older. The results of the analysis are seen in Table 8.7.

Here we come to another frustrating aspect of ANOVA. The sum of squares no longer add up as they did in previous analyses. However, there are two things worth perusing. First, notice that the effect of the covariate Age is significant and that the residual sum of squares here equals the residual sum of squares from the previous analysis minus the sum of squares for Age.

Second, the eta squared for Age (.03), although quite small, may be misleading. How can the variance explained by age be so small when age and income correlate perfectly? We think it is because the explained variance was already saturated by the effects of education and gender: age just could not squeeze in and make its presence felt.

This exercise should illustrate how limiting bivariate statistics can be and how revealing and useful multivariate statistics are.

8.5 Sample ANOVA Procedures

The SPSS-X procedure in Figure 8.1 was used to generate the results from the last example (two factors and one covariate).

TABLE 8.7 ANOVA: Income by Education and Gender with Age

	Sum of Squares	DF	Mean Square	F	Significance
Covariate					
Age	32	1	32	43.73	0.000
Main Effects	59	3	19	27.32	0.000
Education	58	2	29	40.09	0.000
Gender	7	1	7	9.62	0.003
Interactions					
Education/Gender	62	2	32	42.71	0.000
Explained Variance	1021	6	1702	232.71	0.000
Residual	30	41	7		
Total	1051	47	22		

NOTE: The values under Sum of Squares and Mean Square are rounded and represent the actual value times 1,000,000. For example, the actual Sum of Squares for the Main Effects was 1,051,666,666.667 on SPSS-X.

SAS provides a myriad of choices for ANOVA under PROC GLM and is more palatable to the advanced statistician.

ANOVA INCOME BY EDUCATE (1,3), GENDER (1,2) WITH AGE

FIGURE 8.1 Sample ANOVA Procedure from SPSS-X

CHAPTER 9

Factor Analysis

Factor analysis is not one simple technique, but rather a series of techniques that, in the hands of sophisticated users, can reveal a great deal of useful information about the relationships in data and its underlying structure. Since there are whole texts written on factor analysis, all that we can do here is give you a simple overview of the most common applications and a few basic guidelines for decisions. In factor analysis, unlike multiple regression analysis, there is no dependent or criterion variable, just a set of variables about a group of people. These will allow you to look at your data in new ways.

Factor analysis is a statistical technique for examining the commonalities and uniquenesses within a set of more than two variables. A simple statement of the basic non-mathematical assumptions would be that the variables you have measured and recorded are your best representation of some underlying factors or constructs that you are trying to measure, and that they are fewer in number than the variables. For example, to assess patients on admission to an inpatient psychiatric facility, you have a lengthy admission interview to collect information on the patient's age, gender, number of prior hospitalizations, score on depression scales, marital status, and standard personality profiles. No one of these variables could be used to explain why the patient needed to be hospitalized. Some combination of descriptions of precipitating incidents or behavior might be persuasive, but the underlying condition of the patient is partially and imper-

143

fectly described by each of the variables from the interview. If you were to do admissions interviews of several hundred patients and wanted to find if there were different subgroups among them and also to know which of the variables from the interviews were most helpful in classifying them, you might choose factor analysis.

In this circumstance, you might use factor analysis as an exploratory technique, attempting to discover what patterns exist in the data. Or you might choose to use it as a confirmatory technique, using your prior knowledge about the topic and the relationships among variables to test a possible model. Your choice would dictate some of the decisions you would make in setting up the analysis. For instance, you might expect the depression scale, the personality test scores, and some of the history of behavior to indicate whether some element of depression is present; that is, the person who has been severely withdrawn or has made a suicidal gesture is likely to score on the extreme end of a depression scale and a personality profile. Thus, it would be reasonable to assume that these variables, both behavioral history and test scores, are measuring parts of an underlying factor of depression. It might also be assumed that someone who is not clinically depressed would have somewhat different scores on these variables.

The variables that you have measured and written down are the *observed variables*. The variables that you are interested in knowing more about and that are imperfectly measured by the observed variables are the *hypothetical variables* or *factors*.

The observed variables that you have collected may measure parts of more than one factor, and the factors may represent clearly more than one of your variables. The factors that represent more than one variable are called *common factors* because they are common to more than one measured variable. Those that represent only one variable are called *unique factors*.

In Chapter 6 we talked about the fact that the mathemati-

cal foundation of most techniques for looking at the relationships among three or more variables is matrix algebra
or matrix manipulation. We begin with a simple matrix in
which each case or person you have studied is represented
by a horizontal row containing all the information about
him or her. In this matrix, each vertical column contains all
the information on one variable, for example the age of everyone in your sample. Factor analysis techniques use either the *correlation matrix,* also known as the *r* matrix,
which is formed of the simple correlation coefficients between variables, or they use the *covariance matrix,* known
as the *c* matrix, which is formed of the coefficients of association between the variables. Coefficients of association are
those that measure the strength of the relationship between the hypothetical factors and the measured variable.
If you standardize your variables, the covariance matrix
and the correlation matrix are identical.

You may be asked to choose which one to use in a computer analysis by the program or one will be chosen by
default, which will be stated in the instructions in the
manual. Because you may use dichotomous variables and
ordinal variables in these procedures, we suggest that you
choose the correlation matrix. Some programs do not allow you to use the covariance matrix, and the correlation
matrix is the more common choice. If you delve deeper
into factor analysis, you can become more sophisticated in
your choice, depending on the problem and your data. In
any case, the decisions we will suggest here will be adequate in the majority of cases.

In order to continue, we need to introduce a more
complicated-sounding vocabulary, because there are certain terms you will need to know in order both to do factor analysis and to understand what the results mean.

Factor analysis mathematically manipulates the matrix
based on your data so as to develop factors that are unique.
When you choose the method by which the program is to
do this, the *rotation method,* you may specify that it be

orthogonal, with factors independent of each other, or *oblique,* if you have some reason to believe the factors, or underlying variables, should be different but related. The reason for the terminology of oblique and orthogonal is that the axes on which orthogonal factors are plotted and around which the values cluster are at right angles to each other, like those on an ordinary graph you would draw on a piece of graph paper. In oblique rotation, since the factors are correlated rather than independent, the axes are at oblique angles to each other. Just as we suggested that you use stepwise inclusion in multiple regression if you have no strong prior theory on the relationships of the variables, so in factor analysis, we suggest you use orthogonal rotation.

Other decisions will involve the number of factors you want to retain in your final solution and the minimum value you are willing to accept in an *eigenvalue,* or characteristic root. An eigenvalue is a mathematical property of a matrix that accounts for a certain proportion of the variance in it. It is composed of *eigenvectors,* which, in an orthogonal solution, are the correlation coefficients between the factors, which are the underlying hypothetical variables and the observed variables that you have measured, collected, and coded. By looking at the eigenvectors, you can see which variables—those with the highest coefficients—most clearly represent the underlying factors. Obviously, if you start with 30 variables and end up with 5 factors that represent all the variance in your data and that have strong coefficients (eigenvectors) on some variables and small or zero coefficients on others, you have reduced the complexity of your data a lot.

9.1 When to Use Factor Analysis

Unlike the techniques discussed earlier—analysis of variance and multiple regression analysis—factor analysis re-

quires no assumptions about the nature of the relationship between variables. There is no preliminary model of
how one variable predicts or classifies another to be con-
structed, nor will factor analysis tell you which variable
predicts which other one. Indeed, it assumes lack of causality. In its exploratory role, it will help to simplify the
structure of the data by developing a more limited number of factors than variables. Among them, they will explain all the variance in your data. By using these factors
instead of variables in further analysis, you will be able to
use all the information you have but represent it by fewer
variables. When we get to the "how to do it" section, we
will explain which decision rules will help you to reduce
the number of factors even further and give you a more
powerful analysis, one more likely to find any real differences in relationships that exist.

The assumptions necessary to use factor analysis are:

- mostly interval-level variables,
- any nominal variables converted to dichotomous
  dummy variables, and
- a sufficiently large number of cases.

In addition, you should be looking for information about
what the hypothetical variables, or factors, are that provide the basis for your observed variables.

Use of this technique will give you information about
how variables cluster together and about the strength of
the relationship between each measured variable and the
underlying factors.

Beginning users of factor analysis are usually intrigued
with the way the technique confirms what they have
learned from months of theorizing and examining their
data and with the way it adds new information. We hope
you will find this to be true for you.

9.2 How to Do Factor Analysis

Above, we defined some terms that will be helpful to you in reading the sections on factor analysis in the computer manuals, and the information in this chapter will enable you to do a simple factor analysis using the most commonly appropriate default choices. But there are many terms that are not defined here, including methods of extraction and rotation, and in order to expand your range of choices of methods, you will need a better understanding of the mathematical complexities of factor analysis than we can offer here. Some further readings that will help you are listed at the end of the chapter.

You cannot do multivariate analysis techniques such as factor analysis without a computer. Hand calculations, even on such simple data as that used in Chapter 8 on social workers' education and income, are time consuming, difficult, and subject to multiple errors. Therefore, the examples we use will be for SAS and SPSS-X. A review of the section on how to treat missing values from Chapter 6 will help before we look at how to select the procedures to do factor analysis.

Your basic task is to search for the simplest structure that fits the observed data and adequately represents it. Therefore, the purpose of rotation is to find the minimum number of factors that fit the data. In order to do this in any program, you must use some criterion to decide how many factors will reasonably represent your data. You might do this by specifying the number of common factors you want the program to extract, based on what seem to be natural groupings. If your sample from the psychiatric hospital seemed to include three main groups—such as manic depressive, unipolar depressive, and not clinically depressed—you would instruct the program to extract three factors and then examine them to see if they did indeed represent these three groups by the relative weights of the variables you had collected on each factor. Another way you might do this is giving a criterion by which the final number of factors would be selected. If you were not sure how many diagnostic categories there were, you might select an *extraction criterion,* some standard by which you limit the number of factors, by stating that you wanted to include only eigenvalues equal to or greater than 1. This is a commonly used criterion and essentially states that smaller eigenvalues can be discarded without great loss of information.

Since we assume that the reader of this section has little or no familiarity with factor analysis, we are going to suggest that you begin by using a related technique which is not strictly speaking true factor analysis: *principal components analysis.* The two statistical packages we are using for examples treat it somewhat differently. Both include principal components analysis as the default procedure in their factor programs. SAS also separates it out as PROC PRINCOM, a separate procedure from PROC FACTOR. Both have it readily available. We suggest that you use it initially because its results are easier to understand and may guide you through the meaning of it better.

Principal components analysis includes all the data, makes the factors orthogonal to each other (that is, independent of each other), and orders them so that the first principal component, or unrotated factor, accounts for the largest amount of the variance in the data, the second for the next largest, and so on. This, though a separate procedure from true factor analysis, will give you a great deal of information about your data.

All of the standard programs have made some choices and incorporated them as *default options.* They will be the method used unless you change them in your procedure statements. On any of these decisions, the suggestion we make is to use the default options, at least at the beginning, unless you have a strong reason to override them. As you become more familiar with the techniques, you can choose other variations if the results you get from your data indicate that a change is necessary. The computer program manuals explain the options they offer, and some give reasons for choosing certain options.

Starting the procedure is as simple as setting up a SAS or SPSS-X data set with your data (see Chapter 2) and, after cleaning it up, running frequencies and checking your data. Then simply go to the appropriate chapter in the manual and use the simplest form of the procedure statement. For SAS this would be

```
PROC FACTOR;
```

This performs the default, principal components analysis, as the method of extraction of factors, does no rotations, and puts no limit on the number of factors. If no limit is placed on the number of factors, there can be as many factors as variables. If you want descriptive statistics on your data as part of the output, simply expand the statement to read

```
PROC FACTOR SIMPLE CORR;
```

This will also print the means and standard deviations of each variable and the correlations between each pair of variables. You can also get these statistics and a great many more if you use the command

```
PROC FACTOR ALL;
```

which will print every statistic available to the program on your data.

For those of us who understand better by seeing things graphically displayed, a useful option is the *scree plot,* or a plot of the relative sizes of the eigenvalues. It is included if you specify ALL or SCREE in the PROC FACTOR statement. When the eigenvalues are plotted, there is normally a descending line that levels off at a low point. This "break" in the scree plot can be used as a criterion for the number of factors to use in further analysis or to reach a final solution.

The equivalent procedure command in SPSS-X is

FACTOR VARIABLES=VAR1 to VAR6

---

where "VAR1 to VAR6" stands for the names of your variables. In SPSS-X, if you want the simple statistics of mean, standard deviation, and correlation matrix printed, you add another line typed at least one space in from the left margin that says

---

PRINT=UNIVARIATE CORRELATION

---

or, if you want all the statistics, it becomes

FACTOR VAR=VAR1 to VAR6/PRINT=ALL

The primary difference in these two basic approaches is that the default in SPSS-X, if you do not specify an extraction method, is a principal components analysis that is rotated to a principal factor solution using the VARIMAX rotation, the orthogonal rotation which allows for the maximum variance present in the data. With the default factor statement in SAS, your data will not rotate beyond the principal components solution.

Among the many choices in the programs, there are some that will make interpreting the output easier. One of them is the SPSS-X FORMAT subcommand that allows you to list the final factor loadings, the coefficients of individual variables on each factor, and descending order of size. It can also suppress loadings below some criterion you select, such as .30. This makes it much easier to read.

9.3 What Do the Results Mean?

We will use the data on age, education, income, and gender that was the example in Chapter 8 so that you can see the different information you can gain from each technique. Because there were only 24 cases and four variables, we have added two more variables—Years Working in the Field and Years Since Highest Degree—and collected information on 18 more people. Thus we have a total of six variables on 42 people, a little scanty for the rules of thumb we mentioned earlier, but adequate for the sake of example.

There is one case in which the number of years working in the field is missing. If we use it with the default treatment of missing values, listwise deletion, the case will be excluded from the analysis. In this situation, since the case is a B.A.-level worker who is younger and has received her degree more recently than the average in the sample, substituting the mean value for all cases doesn't seem a good option. Since we have only 42 cases and have all other variables on her, neither does excluding the case. Therefore, we decided to use the other option, pairwise deletion, that uses all nonmissing values in this case. We

TABLE 9.1 Means and Standard Deviations for Factor Analysis

Variable	Mean	Standard Deviation	Cases
Years Worked	11.37	6.71	41
Gender	.52	.51	42
Education	18.67	2.52	42
Income	20,300.00	5,702.00	42
Age	37.52	7.53	42
Years Since Graduation	7.76	6.57	42

also requested all statistics. This may give you more information than you want to know, but this is a chance to point out the usefulness of many of them in learning more about your data. Asking for all statistics gave us first the mean, standard deviation, and number of cases on which they were computed, as seen in Table 9.1.

In order to get these results, we recoded Education from the nominal categories of B.A. = 1, M.A. = 2, and Ph.D. = 3 to interval-level data by substituting the number of years normally required to earn each degree, 16, 18, and 22 respectively. Some may disagree with this, but to us it is an acceptable equivalent that increases the power of our data in this type of analysis. Most variables that are ordinal or nominal are not so easily transformed in a logical fashion, but where it is possible we urge you to do it.

The other nominal variable, Gender, has no interval-level equivalent, so it has been coded as a 0-1 dummy variable. The mean (.52) is not a useful interpretation of this variable. It is, however, the percentage of males in the whole sample. Men are coded as 1 and women as 0, and the mean is computed by dividing this total of all the scores in the sample by the number of valid cases, 42.

The next statistic printed is the correlation matrix, which gives correlations between each pair of variables.

TABLE 9.2 Correlation Matrix on Factor Example

	Education	Gender	Income	Age	Years Graduate	Years Working
Education	1.00					
Gender	−.05	1.00				
Income	.75	−.02	1.00			
Age	.44	−.05	.69	1.00		
Years Since Graduation	−.12	−.04	.29	.58	1.00	
Years Working	.41	.05	.70	.90	.60	1.00

As you can see in Table 9.2, the most difficult to interpret and the one with the weakest correlation overall is Gender, a converted nominal variable, with each of the other variables.

Income, the variable of interest in the analysis of variance, is most strongly correlated with Education and then, in descending order, with Years Working, Age, Years Since Graduation, and, trailing far behind, Gender. This latter correlation is so low as to be meaningless. This table is presented in the standard format for correlation matrices. The table shows only the lower/left half of the whole matrix since the scores on the upper/right half would be the same. For example there is no score for Gender in the vertical Income column, since it would be –.02, the score for Income in the vertical Gender column. Each score shown is the correlation between two variables, the column variable and the row variable. Repeating them would be redundant.

Another statistic that is available with both packages is a *measure of sampling adequacy* (MSA). This is a summary of how small the partial correlations are in relation to the simple correlations and warns if there are problems with the variables. For our data, the MSA is a somewhat marginal but usable .68. It is best if it is over .80. If it is less than

.50, something needs to be done to correct it. The measure of sampling adequacy for each individual variable again indicates that the problem is Gender, with an MSA of .08. The MSAs for the others range from .54 to .74. The corrective action is either to drop the offending variable if it is not crucial to your analysis or to add other variables related to it if it is important. Since Gender is the only dummy variable (which may be problematic in correlation analyses), there are no other variables to add that would represent the same dimension, but since it is one we feel important to include in the analysis, we will keep it and proceed with caution.

The next important part of the output from the computer factor program is the first principal components analysis table. Since we did not use any of the criteria mentioned earlier to restrict the number of components, such as specifying a minimum eigenvalue or a maximum number of factors, the program has given us the same number of principal components as we have variables, namely, six. However, the first one accounts for 53.5 percent of the variance in the data, the first three account for 91.5 percent and the first four for 96.1 percent.

This is a point where we could start making decisions about simplification of the data. By looking at the next output, the scree plot shown in Figure 9.1, we can see that the choice of three or four for the number of factors would make sense.

The break in the line is after the fourth eigenvalue, but even that one accounts for less than five percent of the variance. If you thought that the important variable might be Education Level, you might choose three components since there are three levels of that variable. Indeed, the principal components analysis has done that, because at this stage it has used the default using only those eigenvalues larger than 1, the first three, which among them account for a total of 91.5 percent of the variance in the data.

In the factor matrix, which is shown in Table 9.3, the

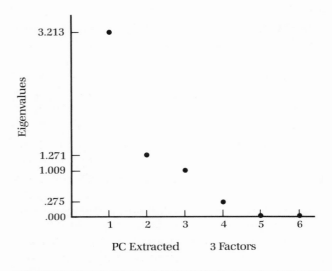

FIGURE 9.1 Scree Plot of Principal Components

numbers printed are the correlations between the observed variables and the underlying factors, or hypothesized variables. Variables found on individual factors are said to *load* together.

This factor matrix tells us that Factor 1 and Factor 2 are common factors for Years Since Graduation, that Factor 1

TABLE 9.3 Factor Matrix

	Factor 1	*Factor 2*	*Factor 3*
Years			
Worked	.73		
Age	.93		
Years Since			
Graduation	.58	.74	
Education	.62	− .74	
Income	.87	− .34	
Gender			.99

is highly correlated with Age and Income, less highly with Years Worked and Education, and about at the same level with Years Since Graduation, and that Factor 3 is correlated only with Gender. Had we not chosen the option on SPSS-X to exclude small correlations, in this case those less than .30, correlations would have been printed for all variables with all factors. The process of ordering them and suppressing small correlations makes the output easier to read and interpret. Factor 2 seems interpretable as representing largely a high positive correlation with Years Since Graduation, a high negative correlation with Education, and a negative correlation with Income, indicating that Factor 2 is possibly B.A.-level workers who have been out of school longer yet earn less.

There is a table in the output that lists the reproduced correlation matrix after the extraction of the eigenvalues, the communalities of the variables, and the residuals between the original observed correlations and the reproduced correlations. The communalities are the scores which show variables as highly correlated with more than one factor. The observed correlations are the original ones and the reproduced correlations are those derived by this procedure. In our data, the communalities are high, .88 to .99, and the residuals are relatively small. The reproduced correlations are very similar to the observed correlations. The program next uses the default VARIMAX rotation, one of several orthogonal techniques, to test successive ways of reducing the data and simplifying it. This occurs as a default in SPSS-X and if you request it in SAS. In exploratory factor analysis, even when variables are highly intercorrelated, as these obviously are, the information gained about the underlying simplified structure of the data is worth obtaining.

The VARIMAX rotation produces a rotated factor matrix where, as in Table 9.3, the coefficients represent the correlation between the variables and the factors. Table 9.4 shows these final coefficients are somewhat different, but Factor 3 still represents only Gender. Since the output

TABLE 9.4 Rotated Factor Matrix

	Factor 1	Factor 2	Factor 3
Years Since Graduation	.93		
Years Working	.81	.49	
Age	.79	.51	
Education		.96	
Income	.41	.84	
Gender			.99

indicates this factor accounts for 21% of the variance in the data, it was worth retaining in the analysis even with its earlier weak showing.

If you compare Table 9.4 with Table 9.3, you will see that on the unrotated matrix some variables are positive and some negative. This gives the direction as well as the strength of the correlations between the observed variables and the underlying factors. On Factor 2 in the unrotated matrix, two of the correlations are negative and one positive, which allows us, knowing the meanings of the variables, to speculate that this factor might well represent the B.A.-level workers who have lower average salaries and, by definition, fewer years of schooling. The rotated factor matrix, which shows the strength but not the direction of the correlations between variables and factors, shows that Education is now correlated above .30 (remember, we chose an option that suppressed smaller correlations) only with Factor 2, and at a .96 level. Factor 3 is a unique factor for gender. Factor 1 contains correlations with three variables at above .50: Age, Years Since Graduation, and Years Working. This could certainly be interpreted as an age and experience factor. Factor 2 has correlations above our cutoff with four of the variables, but the two that are substantially stronger than the others are Education and Income, which, here as in most studies, are highly intercorrelated. You could interpret them as a socioeconomic status factor. These interpretations are looser than those you would do on your own more complex and interesting data, but they can give you an idea of what factor analysis can do for you.

We started this process with six variables describing people, perhaps the demographic section of the study data. We have ended up with three factors that adequately represent over 91% of the variance in the data, that are interpretable, and that may be substituted for the six variables in further analysis. They also make sense in explaining the data and in pointing out relationships that exist among the variables. A great deal of information can be gained about any study by doing this one procedure.

References that are particularly helpful in further explanation of factor analysis of nonstatistically-minded people are the two volumes by Jae-On Kim and Charles Mueller (1978). Several of the general multivariate texts also have good explanations of the theory of factor analysis.

CHAPTER 10

Discriminant Function Analysis

Discriminant function analysis is a technique for distinguishing among two or more groups defined by one classification variable with multiple levels, and judging the relative importance of several other variables in forming that distinction. The classification, or grouping, variable is assumed to be nominal in level and the other variables to be interval or continuous.

This information can be used to discover relative influence and, once you have determined that, to predict membership of a given case in a group or class. Like several other techniques we have discussed, the computer programs written to perform this one allow you to save information generated by the procedure and to use it in later procedures. If, in the data on education, income, and so on used in the chapters on analysis of variance and factor analysis, you wanted to be able to distinguish among the three educational levels and to see the relative influence of the other variables on your ability to do so, you would use discriminant function analysis. If there was a group of people for whom you knew all of the characteristics in the data except educational level, you could use the information gained in the exploratory phase to estimate what their educational level was.

In our example in earlier chapters of admission data at a psychiatric hospital, if diagnostic category were your variable of interest, you could make that your grouping or classification variable and test the relative influence of your test, demographic, and history data on it. Once you had done this at a level that correctly classified a satisfactory proportion of your cases, you could use that data to classify new intakes on the basis of the most important information as demonstrated by the discriminant function analysis. This could assist in diagnostic assessments, especially for inexperienced workers. Although results from statistical techniques such as those discussed in this book will never take the place of professional knowledge, experience, and judgment, they are a useful adjunct to it, a way of classifying what we know and using that classification to help discover what we don't know.

Although any nominal categorical variable can be used as your classification variable, you must consider your sample size. For instance, common sense tells that if we are trying to classify people into ethnic groups on the basis of their values and attitudes, we should have some minimum number of people in each group in order to do it with any degree of certainty. If you are looking at a classification or criterion variable that has ten possible categories, a sample of 50 cases would allow an average of only 5 cases per category, with the likelihood that there would be some categories with 2 cases and some with 10. Your predictive ability would not be very good. You also need enough variables that potentially describe your groups to provide adequate information for prediction.

In other words, discriminant function analysis is a procedure for classifying cases into categories when you have enough information about the characteristics of all cases to make prediction reasonably probable.

Since this technique will develop (K–1) discriminant functions, or one less function than the number of categories of your classification variable, it will derive anything from one function for a two-category variable, such as gender, to nine functions for ten category-variable, such as ethnic groups in a certain part of the world. You can use it with even more categories, but it becomes unwieldy and increasingly difficult to interpret.

Here as elsewhere in the book, we will not talk about the mathematics involved in the computation; that will be left to the computer program. We will only note that in the simplest two-category classification variable instance, the computation is the equivalent of a multiple regression analysis with a dummy dependent variable, something we told you not to do. If you encounter this problem, the treatment of choice is discriminant function analysis since you are not violating any assumptions as to levels of measurement or degrees of freedom and are well within the logic of the technique and its interpretation.

One main advantage of using this technique to distinguish among groups is that quite often groups that are not clearly distinguishable on a variable-by-variable basis are quite different when examined from a multivariate point of view. The contribution of each variable to this difference may be small but crucial.

10.1 When to Use Discriminant Analysis

Because it is so often necessary in human services to make broad judgments about what category people or problems fit into in order to provide service, it is helpful to be able to use information already gathered on the characteristics of the people or problems in those classes.

Suppose you have a waiting list for your new self-sufficiency and peer support program for people with problems of substance abuse. Your program is so revolutionary that everyone who has completed it has stayed free from chemical dependency for at least one year. However, almost a third of those who entered the program in the first two years dropped out. You have some guesses as to what might be different about the two groups. The average age of the drop-outs is lower; you think more of them might have been referred by law enforcement agencies; and they had less prior therapy experience or more years of addiction. Wouldn't it be terrific to be able to see which of those (or other) characteristics predict success? Wouldn't it be great to be able to look at those characteristics at intake and use them to help select program participants? Of course the results won't be perfect, since they are based on probabilities, not certainties, but if you could accurately predict program completion in 80% to 90% of your referrals, you'd be doing a lot better than your current track record. You also would be reducing the odds of using precious program resources on those who would be less likely to benefit from them.

It sometimes seems unethical or distasteful to human service providers to use something other than their own judgment to make decisions about people. If you are satisfied with the results of using your own judgment only, by all means continue to do so. However, it is often helpful to have additional information when making difficult decisions, and that is what discriminant function analysis in its classification role can give us.

To use discriminant function analysis in an exploratory role, we would take all the information about program participants that seemed significant and use it to develop the model for the classification phase. Remember the assumptions necessary for multivariate analysis that we discussed in Chapter 6? They involved the level of measurement of the data, sufficient numbers of cases, and the underlying distribution of the data. In the case of discriminant function analysis, the assumptions are:

- nominal-level classification or criterion variables,
- interval-level independent or predictor variables,
- a sufficient number of cases, and
- a multivariate normal distribution.

Note that this is the first type of analysis in which we

have stressed multivariate normal distribution. Most of the other statistics are quite robust and tolerate some variations in that assumption. Discriminant function analysis in its classic form cannot. You probably don't know if you have a multivariate normal distribution. However, it can be assumed if you have all continuous variables or variables that can be assumed to have equal intervals and many intermediate points (which makes them interval-level variables). Strong ordinal variables and dichotomous dummy variables don't meet those criteria. Think about plotting a line on a number of cases on the relationship between Gender and Income. Income is a continuous interval-level variable, but Gender is not. Gender has only two possible values, Male and Female, and therefore only two possible points on your plot. What you would get in this hypothetical plot is two sets of points, each distributed along the values of Income. This would not fit an assumption of a multivariate normal distribution.

However, if you do not have a multivariate normal distribution, or think you don't because you have dichotomous dummy variables as independent variables, such as presence or absence of certain symptoms, or ordinal-level variables, such as ratings of level of pathology or severity of substance abuse problems, there is a variation of discriminant function analysis, called nearest neighbors, that can still be used. Because of our assumptions about the kinds of data you are likely to have, that is the one we are going to discuss further here. Even if you have all interval data and a multivariate normal distribution, however, you can still follow the discussion, since the procedures are similar and in the same sections of the computer manuals. The difference lies in the mathematical computations you are asking the computer to do.

The variation we are suggesting is a set of procedures which rely on each case's physical geometrical difference in space from other cases and thus are called *nearest neighbors*. The assumption is that cases that are neighbors and closest to each other on the plot have more in common than those that are farther away. Using the criterion of near neighbors, the cases are classified into the number of categories specified by your classification variable. Optionally, you can ask for the probability of each case being classified into each category or into the closest categories. Especially when you are developing the classification scheme, it is useful to have the list of cases printed out, each with its actual category, predicted category, and the probability of its being in the other categories. This allows you to look at the individual cases that are misclassified and find out by looking at the information on John or Mary in what way they differ from the other people in their category. This may allow you to decide to collect additional information to improve your classification model. The ability to go back on a case-by-case basis and see what discriminates is one of the most useful features of the discriminant function analysis techniques. Even if the variables in your analysis are highly correlated within your groups, a condition that can wreak havoc in bivariate analysis, discriminant function analysis will be able to distinguish them.

10.2 How to Do Discriminant Analysis

Again, we will give examples from two major statistical packages, SPSS-X and SAS. (Most other packages available at university computing centers also have similar routines for performing this type of analysis.) On the earlier techniques we discussed, the two packages are, for the most part, equivalent and offer the same range of options in the procedures, at least at the beginning level. In discriminant function analysis, however, there is more of a difference in the choices you can make, especially if you do not have a multivariate normal distribution in your data.

10.2.1 Nonparametric Discriminant Techniques

SAS has a set of four procedures, PROC DISCRIM, PROC NEIGHBOR, PROC CANDISC, and PROC STEPDISC. PROC NEIGHBOR is the one that is a nonparametric equivalent procedure and allows violation of the assumption of a multivariate normal distribution. The other three assume that, although the classification variable is a nominal categorical one, the other variables are all continuous interval-level with a multivariate normal distribution within each class.

The equivalent program in SPSS-X is one procedure, DISCRIMINANT, which has fewer options available. It does, however, allow you to choose a method option of *Mahalanobis distance* between groups, which is a nearest-neighbor nonparametric procedure. SAS, in its NEIGHBOR procedure, allows you a choice of *Euclidean distance* as well as Mahalanobis distance. We will not attempt to explain these terms here or the mathematics involved in them; if you want to learn more about them, consult the references at the end of the chapter or an advanced text on multivariate statistics. Suffice it to say that we recommend that you use the default, the Mahalanobis distance, in SAS's PROC NEIGHBOR; this is the only choice offered you for nearest neighbors in SPSS-X.

10.2.2 Choosing the Probabilities for Categories

One additional thing to think about is how you want the procedure to decide how many cases belong in each category of your classification variable. Both programs assume that each category has the same number of cases unless you tell them otherwise, and they will base their classification attempts on that assumption.

If you have a data set on intake information from the psychiatric hospital that contains 90 cases, 40 of whom are schizophrenic, 20 of whom are bipolar depressives, 10 of whom are in a severe depressive episode, and 20 of whom are a collection of other diagnostic categories, since the program does not know what your codes mean, it will assume that one-fourth of them are in each of the categories unless you specify otherwise. In actuality in the data cited above, about 45%, almost half, are diagnosed as schizophrenics.

If you don't specify proportions, the program will try to reclassify a good proportion of them as something else, because its assumption is that the number of cases in each category is the same. Each of the programs has a simple way to handle this. They each have a statement on prior probability that you can specify as using the actual proportion of cases on the classification variable categories, or choose other numbers to represent probabilities. If you are classifying data for which you know the categories, it seems obviously simpler to use the statement saying that the program should use that information. If you are using data from an earlier procedure or new data for which you know everything but the classification variable (in this case, diagnostic category), you might want to use the proportions found in your earlier data by specifying those percentages.

10.2.3 Procedure Commands for Discriminant Function

We are going to use the data on education, income, gender, and so on one more time. Although it may seem monotonous, using it again has two advantages. You will have an opportunity to see how different procedures gain somewhat different information from the same data, and the data is simple enough to allow you to interpret the results without any specialized theoretical knowledge base. We hope that this will help you when you choose which techniques to use on your own data and interpret them. In fact, we encourage you to try several techniques on your own data, keeping in mind the assumptions necessary for their use.

Remember that we have done several data transformations on these data earlier, using both education and gender as either nominal- or interval-level variables, depending on how we defined them. In this example, we are using Education as the three-category nominal classification variable, and have defined Gender as a 0–1 nominal dichotomous dummy variable, which we are including as a predictor. In other words, we are attempting to discover the relative influence of the other variables in predicting educational level and to see if the procedure can classify them correctly. Let's try it.

The program commands for SPSS-X to do a nonparametric nearest-neighbors discriminant function analysis on these data are shown below. The first statement calls for the discriminant procedure and defines the classification or grouping variable. The numbers in parentheses after the variable name are the lowest and highest values of the grouping variable. The next statement says which variables are to be used as predictors in this analysis. Obviously, this cannot include the grouping variable since it would provide a perfect prediction of group membership. The third statement is the method statement, which tells the procedure to use the geometric Mahalanobis distance of cases to classify them, since we do not think we have a multivariate normal distribution. If you think that your data do represent such a distribution, simply omit this statement and the procedure will use the default direct entry method for all variables. There are also other choices that you can select by reading the SPSS-X manual.

```
DISCIMINANT GROUPS = EDUCATE (1,3)
    VARIABLES = GENDER TO YRSWRK/
    METHOD = MAHAL/
    PRIORS = SIZE/
OPTIONS 8
STATISTICS  1  2  3  4  13  14  15
```

The fourth line of this program (PRIORS = SIZE) directs

the program to use the actual proportion of cases in each value of the grouping variable, education, to select the number of cases in each category on the final results. Since this procedure uses listwise deletion (omitting any case with a missing value on any variable) and does not allow the options of pairwise deletion or substituting a mean score for the missing value, it will not use the case with a missing value on the number of years in the field to develop the classification scheme. However, it will classify it in the final table, using the information that it has. Therefore, we have 41 cases to use to develop the classification scheme, 13 B.A.'s and 14 each with M.A. and Ph.D. degrees. We included the case with the missing value in the final classification table by specifying Option 8 in the fifth line of the program. On the sixth and final line, we have selected a number of statistics to aid us in interpreting our results. We have asked for group means and standard deviations, the pooled correlation matrix, the classification results table, a case-by-case listing of original group membership and the group to which it is assigned, and a combined plot of all three groups, which will show us each case represented by its group number and the centroid, the central point in the distribution of each group. The classification table, plot, and case-by-case listing are extremely informative, as we shall see below.

In order to get similar output from SAS, the program is somewhat shorter since many of the commands are included in the procedure statement as you can see.

```
PROC NEIGHBOR LIST; CLASS EDUCATE;
VAR GENDER—YRSWRK; PRIORS PROP;
```

This will not produce a plot, correlation matrix, or group means and standard deviations since these options are not available with this procedure. It will, however, give you the prior probabilities of group membership, the case-by-case listing of the class to which each case belongs and the one to which it was classified, and the final results classification table.

10.3 What Do the Results Mean?

Like the procedures described in earlier chapters, the SPSS-X commands written for discriminant analysis allow you to generate simple statistics about your data, in this case means and standard deviations of each predictor variable by groups. SPSS-X also optionally allows you to print correlation and covariance matrices. We will not go over the usefulness of these again, or print their results, since we did so in earlier chapters, and the interpretation is the same regardless of the procedure used to generate these statistics.

The SPSS-X procedure used a stepwise selection procedure and a criterion of statistical significance, Wilk's lambda, for including predictor variables in the analysis. Using this method, it included only Age, Income, and Years Since Graduation as predictors. The procedure determined that, after using these, Gender and Years Working did not add sufficient additional information to the ability to classify to include them in further calculations. Using this method, the program correctly classified 38 out of 42 cases, 90.48%. The misclassifications were that two master's-level people were classified as Ph.D.'s and two Ph.D.'s were classified as master's level.

The SAS nearest-neighbor procedure did not perform as well on these data nor did it give as much information. It correctly classified 29 out of 42 cases by using all of the predictor variables, a rate of 71.4% correct. The misclassifications were from bachelor's to master's, master's to both bachelor's and doctorates, and doctorates to both bachelor's and master's, although the largest number of misclassifications, four, were from master's to doctorates.

TABLE 10.1 Summary of Variables Entered

Variable	Wilk's Lambda	Significance	Between Groups	
Income	.32855	.000	2	3
Years Since Graduation	.20401	.000	2	3
Age	.18917	.000	1	2

One of the four cases misclassified by SPSS-X was classified correctly by SAS. Because we asked for a listing of the cases, their class membership, and their classification, we are able to see where these errors occurred. By going back to the original data, we can look at what is different about those cases that were misclassified and make decisions about what further information we need to have to improve the classification.

In this analysis, SPSS-X, by eliminating two variables that did not discriminate between the categories to a significant degree, did a better job of classifying correctly than did SAS, which also did a nearest-neighbor procedure but used all the variables. The two variables excluded—Gender and Years Working in the Field—were almost identical in two of the three categories. Both the M.A. and Ph.D. groups were half men and half women, as the B.A. group would have been had it not eliminated one woman because of a missing variable. The mean (average) number of Years Working for M.A.'s was 13.6 and the mean for Ph.D's was 13.9. By looking at the classification results, we can only assume that the additional variables used clouded the issue rather than helped.

Table 10.1 summarizes the process of selecting which variables to include in the SPSS-X analysis by showing not only the significance level for each variable included, but also the groups between which the program discriminates best.

As you can see, the lambda for each entry decreases,

since it represents the amount of information added by the variable being included in that step, after accounting for the information contributed by those entered earlier. You will also note that it was not until the third variable, Age, was entered that anything distinguished Group 1, the B.A.'s, from either of the others. Looking at the mean values by group, we can see that the average age of the B.A.'s is 31.5, while the average age of the M.A.'s is 39.7, and the Ph.D.'s average 40.9. The latter two are quite close, but the distinction between the B.A.'s and the M.A.'s is quite clear.

The SPSS-X program we have written also produces a scatterplot, which is a useful way to examine the relationships among the cases. In this situation, where our classification variable has three categories and therefore there are two (3 – 1) discriminant functions, it is quite easy to interpret. Each case is plotted by its score on each of the two functions, while the centroid of each group is marked by an asterisk. Each case is represented by the number of the group to which it belongs. As you can see in Figure 10.1, not only are the centroids of the three groups clearly separate, but the cases also separate quite well into clusters. If there were not such a clear distinction in the data, the plot would show a more mixed picture.

Probably the single most useful part of the output, which you can obtain from either SAS or SPSS-X, is the classification results table. Since the number of cases classified correctly differ, we have chosen to present the more successful one, the SPSS-X results, seen in Table 10.2. The column on the left hand side of the table, "Actual Group," identifies each group to which the data tell us the cases belong. The row of numbers across the top, "Predicted Group Membership," indicates the groups into which the cases were classified by the procedure, using all the available information except the actual classification. As you can see, even though only age as a variable distinguished clearly between B.A.'s and the other people, all 14 of the

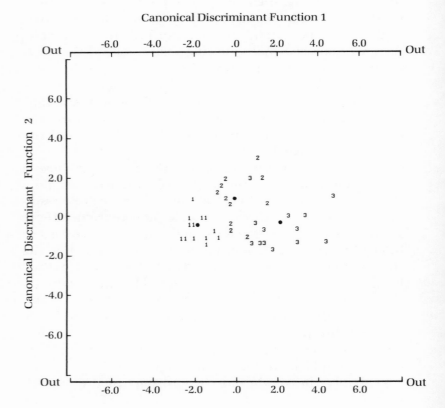

* Indicates a Group Centroid

FIGURE 10.1: Plot of All Cases on Discriminant Functions

TABLE 10.2 Classification Results

Actual	Group	Number of Cases	Predicted Group Membership		
			1	2	3
B.A.	1	14	14	0	0
			100%	0%	0%
M.A.	2	14	0	12	2
			0%	85.7%	14.3%
Ph.D.	3	14	0	2	12
			0%	14.3%	85.7%

Percent of Grouped Cases Correctly Classified: 90.48%

B.A.'s were correctly classified. Looking across the next line, the M.A.'s, you can see that 12 of them were correctly classified and that 2 were classified as Ph.D.'s. Looking at the third line, the Ph.D.'s, again 12 of them were classified correctly and 2 were classified as M.A. level. These are impressive results and indicate what a useful technique this can be in problems involving classification.

Obviously, if you can use information that you already have to develop a way to classify 90% of your cases correctly by using fewer variables, that can be extremely useful in situations where the classification or grouping variable is not known, but the other information is. In the process of developing this classification, you may also discover, as we did in these data, that you need not collect all of the information you thought you might need to discriminate among your groups, which is potentially a great savings in time, money, and effort in collecting, coding, and entering information for your study into the computer.

There is an excellent discussion of discriminant function analysis by William Klecka in the 1975 version of the SPSS manual. He has also written several other books and monographs on the technique that should be helpful to the beginning user.

CHAPTER 11

Loglinear Analysis

In the human services, there are often problems or questions in which all of the characteristics about which we want to inquire are of nominal levels of measurement, or, at best, of limited ordinal level. In the not too distant past, the only way to examine the relationships among them in terms of statistical probabilities was with a series of chi-square analyses. As you may remember from Chapter 4, these are essentially bivariate measures of the strength of associations. When we add another variable, a chi-square table and analysis are done on the first two variables entered by each level of the third variable. For example, if we looked at Education by Gender by Ethnicity, what we would get would be a series of analyses of Education by Gender. The first might be Education by Gender for Whites, then Education by Gender for Blacks, then for Hispanics, and so on. While this is better than not being able to see if there are different patterns of the association of gender and education in different ethnic groups, it does not allow us to look at the interaction effects of gender and ethnicity on educational level. These interaction effects are often quite strong.

11.1 Cross-Classification Techniques

A series of techniques has evolved to examine interactions of multiple nominal variables since the development of high-speed computers and the software to use them for data analysis. A common name for these techniques is the analysis of *cross classifications.* One of the techniques that has received a lot of attention is log linear analysis, which is the focus of this chapter. Although all of these techniques are similar to chi-square in that they examine the relative frequencies of cells that contain the count of the number of black female Ph.D.'s, for example, and use the relationship of that count to the count we would expect given the number of blacks, the number of females, and the number of Ph.D.'s in our sample, mathematically they go about it in somewhat different ways.

In the chapter on bivariate relationships, when we talked about chi-square, we mentioned it as a test of statistical independence. That is, if you have two variables of interest, you are trying to discover if some value in one of them occurs independently of some value in the other. If it does not, if the presence of some value in one affects the values in the other, they are not statistically independent. There is another interpretation or use of the chi-square test, the *goodness-of-fit* model, which proposes a relationship between the variables of characteristics and tests to see if it exists in your data. It is this interpretation, goodness of fit, that is the basis for the measures of the relationships between more than two nominal level variables that we are discussing in this chapter.

This becomes much more interesting as you add more than two variables, because you can propose not only a relationship where each variable is important, but also relationships where the interactions between two or more variables are important in themselves. Gender may be a powerful variable in predicting occupational level. So may educational level or ability in a particular skill area such as mathematics. However, the interaction of Gender and Interest in Mathematics may be much more powerful in explaining occupational level than either one of those variables alone would be. The techniques discussed in this chapter allow us to test that possibility.

Since all the variables are assumed to be nominal level

and expressed in frequencies, there is no assumption of a multivariate normal distribution or, of course, of continuous variables. You don't have to worry about the shape of your underlying distribution, since the techniques look only at your sample and what could be expected from looking at it.

Again, since cross-classification techniques only examine your sample, there is no assumption of independent random sampling, since the category totals, or *marginals,* are used to predict how many cases should be in each cell. A 2-by-2 table, one with two nominal variables, such as Gender and Religion, each of which you have defined as having two possible values such as Male and Female for Gender, obviously enough, and Christian and Other for Religion, would have four marginals, the totals of each line across and each column down. The marginals would be the number of men, the number of women, the number of Christians, and the number of Other. There is also, of course, a grand total, the number of cases. Cells or *cell frequencies* are the total number of cases in each crosstabulated category within the table, the number of Christian women, the number of Christian men, the number of Other women and the number of Other men.

11.2 Loglinear Analysis

A commonly used cross-classification technique, *loglinear analysis,* is a chi-square-based measure that allows for the measurement of the strength of the interactions of several variables rather than being limited to the two or three nominal-level variables used in standard chi-square procedures. By so doing, it attempts to identify the structure underlying a set of categorical variables. Identifying this structure allows you to understand the relationship between the variables in your data, and perhaps to predict, by a model derived from the data, the relationships in a

similar circumstance involving the same variables. That
is, if the relationships and interactions are those postulated in a given model, it is probable that the results in the
actual table would be those found in other similar data.

The relationship that you assume exists in the data is
stated as a "model," or hypothesized relationship. This
can take the form of a statement like salary level equals education plus experience plus gender plus age, or education equals (gender × education) + experience + age. In a
model statement like this you would use salary level as the
criterion variable and the others as predictor variables to
use the terminology introduced earlier. In the second example you are stating that the interaction between gender
and education is one of the predictor variables. In loglinear, what we called the criterion variable earlier is often called the *response variable.*

The procedure computes estimated expected cell frequencies by a method called *iterative proportional fitting.*
This procedure involves the selection of preliminary estimates of the expected cell frequencies, and then the successive adjustment of them until they satisfy the criterion
that all marginal totals of the estimates equal the marginal
totals of the observed frequencies (Reynolds, 1977). The
model is built by successive iterations or adjustments until the maximum degree of significance possible is
achieved. In this it is like factor rotation, discussed in
Chapter 9.

The steps involved in this model-building are explained by Reynolds (1977) as the following:

- Propose a model that might account for the observed
  data. A model is really a hypothesis about how a set of
  variables is distributed and interrelated. It reflects the
  investigator's beliefs about the underlying structure of
  the data.
- Derive a set of expectations under the assumption that
  the model is true. This asks in effect what a set of data

would look like if the model were true. The estimates made under this expectation form the basis for computing the cell frequencies.

- Decide whether the model is acceptable. This stage compares the computed estimates under your proposed model with the observed cell and marginal frequencies and decides whether differences are small enough to be attributed reasonably to chance or whether the model is not an acceptable explanation.
- If the discrepancies are sufficiently small, retain the model; otherwise, return to step one.

We also suggest that, after going through this process, you should refine it as far as possible, and then estimate the parameters, translate them into conclusions about the relationships between your variables, and use them to make predictions about further relationships.

11.3 When to Use Loglinear Analysis

The description of loglinear analysis above probably gives you a good idea of when it is appropriate to use it. Like other new techniques for the analysis of cross-classifications, it is a test of goodness of fit in n-way discrete frequency distributions that allows for some measurement of interaction effects. It also, through the proportionate iterative model fitting mentioned above, allows for estimates of the relative importance of several discrete variables or of combinations of them.

It is this ability to look at the relative importance of interactions that makes it so intriguing and useful. In the example of black female Ph.D.'s above, if their salary is lower (or higher) than the average in their field or if their advancement has been slower or faster than their colleagues', can those variations be attributed to gender or to race discrimination, ability, affirmative action programs, or a combination of all of these? Most often, it is probably some combination of these and other variables. Most of them, you will note, are nominal-level of measurement. This would be a question where you would want to use log linear analysis.

11.3.1 Necessary Assumptions

In contrast to the number of assumptions necessary for some of the techniques discussed earlier, the assumptions for log linear are few and simple. They are:

- a *multinomial distribution,* that is, one with a number of discrete named categories, and
- a fairly large fixed N.

The multinomial distribution is an easy assumption to meet. If you have any continuous-interval variables and wish to use this technique, you must go contrary to all our earlier advice and collapse them into fewer categories by using the "if-then" type of statements or "recode" statements discussed earlier under data transformations. You would only do this, of course, if most of the variables in which you were interested were nominal and you wished to include one or two others. In the example above, you might wish to include income information, but the exact amount of the income might be of less interest to you as a researcher than whether it was above or below the mean for the person's occupation. Thus you could reclassify income figures into high, average, and low or above or below the mean.

Why not just use the actual figures for income and leave the other variables nominal? Almost every beginning statistics student has done this in a computerized data analysis program by entering the variables for a chi-square analysis such as gender, race, degree, and income. When the printout arrives, you have 2 categories for gender, perhaps 3 for race (Black, White, and Other), and 2 for degree. So far you have a 2 × 3 × 2 or 12-cell table. If you have 60 subjects, that gives you an average of 5 per cell, skimpy but probably adequate. If you add income as raw figures, you probably have at least 40 or 50 different exact salaries. Multiply your 12-cell table by even 40 and, you have 480 cells for 60 cases. Even if you collapse to high, medium, and low, you have 36 cells. This gives you an average of fewer than 2 cases per cell. The test will not have enough power to distinguish real relationships that may exist in your data.

The necessity for a fairly large fixed N should be obvious. The chi-square rule of thumb of an expected frequency of 5 cases per cell is something to keep in mind here. It is not a hard-and-fast rule, but violate it with caution. In fact, try to exceed it whenever possible. For log linear analysis, 10 or 12 cases per cell are better.

11.4 How to Do Loglinear Analysis

Again, we will give you sample programming statements from SAS and SPSS-X to get you started in trying out these procedures. Since there has been so much interest in developing techniques to study multiple nominal-level characteristics over the past 20 years or so, there have been a number of specialized procedures written that do only these types of analysis. Some of them may be available at your local college or university computer center. If so, they may be worth looking into. One of the standard statistical packages that we have not discussed in this book, the BMDP package from the University of California at Los Angeles, has an especially well-written set of procedures for log linear analysis. If you have access to it, we suggest you look at it.

In SAS, the procedure that performs loglinear analysis

is PROC FUNCAT, which stands for functions of categorical responses. With it, you can specify response and design effects, much as you would in analysis of variance. In this procedure there are no options to use with the PROC statement except that of naming the data set to be used. As always in SAS, if you don't name a particular data set, it uses the last one created; in other words, it normally uses your input data set unless you have changed it in some way that creates a new set, such as doing a factor analysis and writing an OUT= statement putting the factor scores in a new data set. There would be no reason for you to do that with nominal data, so we assume you haven't and that you are using your input data. In that case, you begin your procedures with PROC FUNCAT.

In addition to this procedure statement, you must use a model statement that defines what you think the relationships in the data are, and which the procedure will then test for individual variable effects and for the effects of any interactions you specify. You may also use ANOVA-type logic and test for nested effects, main effects, and combinations of the two.

Keeping to our practice of giving you an introductory look at each procedure in this book and keeping it simple by using defaults and relatively simple examples, we will specify simple models.

The corresponding procedure (and the procedure command statement) in SPSS-X is LOGLINEAR. What is called a model statement in SAS is called a design statement in SPSS-X. In SPSS-X, you do not have to specify a design statement, but if you do not, the program will test only for the *saturated model,* which means it will test all independent variables and all possible interactions. It will not, however, see any variable as a response variable or expect that it needs to check certain interactions against a dependent or response variable. Unless you are on a real fishing expedition, use a design statement to tell the program what relationships to look at.

We are going to use a new data set to test out this procedure for two reasons. The first is that the research question should be one that can be answered using all nominal-level discrete variables. The second is that you need a lot of cases. (Those were the two assumptions we discussed earlier.) The data we are using were collected in a study of unwanted pregnancies in four sites that covered a major urban area, smaller cities, and rural and suburban populations. The study population included both adolescents and women in their twenties and thirties. Their ages were dichotomized into a nominal variable called Teen, which was coded as yes or no. The other variables in the study were nominal dichotomies on whether or not they had family support and involvement in their decisions around the pregnancy, whether they lived in the major urban area or downstate, and whether they decided to place the baby for adoption or keep it. Those who decided on early abortions were excluded from this analysis. Thus, all variables are nominal dichotomies. There were 310 cases in the study and no missing values.

For purposes of this example, we will assume that the question of interest is whether the decision to place or keep the baby is related to whether the mother is an adolescent, whether she received support from her family, and whether she lived in the major urban area or the rural and suburban areas downstate. The program commands to use in SPSS-X to test the assumption that those other variables influence the decision to place are shown below.

```
LOGLINEAR PLACE (1,2) BY FAMILY UPDOWN TEEN (1,2)/
   PRINT=DEFAULT ESTIM/
   CRITERIA=DELTA (.5)/
   DESIGN=UPDOWN, FAMILY, TEEN, PLACE BY UPDOWN,
      PLACE BY FAMILY, PLACE BY TEEN,
      PLACE BY FAMILY BY TEEN, PLACE BY UPDOWN BY FAMILY BY TEEN
```

There are a number of other options in LOGLINEAR that you may choose to use as you become more familiar with the procedure. This is simply a very basic program that will cover the most common problem for which this is a suitable technique, a problem with several nominal variables in which you are interested in testing the relative influence of several independent or predictor variables and their interactions on one dependent criterion or response variable. The first line in the above example calls for the log linear procedure and establishes that the placement decision is the dependent variable by placing it in front of the keyword BY. The numbers in parentheses after the dependent variable and the list of independent variables establish the range of coded values to be used in the analysis. These variables all happen to be nominal dichotomies with all values coded as one or two. If one or more variables had possible codes of three or four, you would place a set of parentheses after that variable with the correct range of lowest value, highest value. The slash at the end of the line lets SPSS-X know that you are continuing the command.

The next line with the PRINT subcommand tells the program that you want it to print the default output, which tells you the observed and expected frequencies for each cell and their residuals, the difference between observed and expected frequencies for each cell. The second specification on the print subcommand asks for parameter estimates for each of the elements of the model you have specified. These parameter estimates are coefficients which may be interpreted somewhat like regression coefficients, as we shall discuss in the section on what the results mean.

The next line, CRITERIA = DELTA(.5), is a precaution against messing up the computations by having empty cells, ones with no cases in them. It is perfectly possible that you might have sufficient cases overall to have an expected cell frequency of five or more but to still have an empty cell, one where there are no cases. In the example here, we might well have no older mothers living downstate who placed their babies for adoption. Since the cell frequencies are used for computation, including division, if they have no cases in them they have a value of zero, and division by zero is, of course, impossible. If you try to make the computer do it, strange and marvelous things may happen, but you won't get the information that you need. The delta subcommand is saying to add the same amount, in this case half a person, to each cell so that none of them is zero. This does not affect the relationship between cells in which you are interested, but it allows them all to be used. It's a good idea to use this specification routinely in LOGLINEAR or other analyses of cross-classifications.

The last part of this routine is the DESIGN= statement in which you say what you think should be tested for its influence on your dependent variable. You will notice that the list includes not only individual independent variables, but also pairs and triads of variables connected by the word BY. These are the interactions we were talking about earlier. The program will test for their effect on the dependent variable just as it tests for each independent variable.

The SAS program that brings approximately the same results as the SPSS-X program cited above is, as in discriminant function analysis, somewhat shorter. So is the output. Either one should be interpretable. We hope that by showing you the language for two statistical packages we can remove some of the magic from the process and make it useful for you.

In SAS, as we mentioned above, the procedure is PROC FUNCAT. The program, after appropriate job control language for the computer installation you are using and the definition of your data set and where the computer can find it is:

```
PROC FUNCAT;
MODEL PLACE=UPDOWN FAMILY TEEN UPDOWN*FAMILY*TEEN
   UPDOWN*FAMILY*TEEN FAMILY*TEEN/ADDCELL=.5
   FREQ PROB ML
```

The model statement is the equivalent of the design statement in SPSS-X. Here the interactions are specified by an * instead of the word BY. The words after the slash in the model statement are options that match those we selected in SPSS-X. The ADDCELL specification is the same as the DELTA in SPSS-X. It adds half a person or case to each cell to avoid the messy problems involved in dividing by zero or taking the log of zero. FREQ asks for the observed and expected frequencies for each cell, with the probabilities expected in each. ML asks for maximum likelihood solutions, the default in SPSS-X, which does the proportionate iterative model fitting mentioned above.

With both of these programs, you will see what frequencies you actually have of downstate teenagers with family support who have placed their babies for adoption—or the observed frequencies—and what each frequency would probably be given the number of teenagers, the number of downstaters, the number with family support, and the number who placed in the entire sample. These observed and expected frequencies and associated tests of significance tell us a lot about the sample. They don't, however, tell us about the interactions among variables. These interactions come in the form of the parameters for each factor you have specified, and they are expressed in the form of coefficients that we will discuss in the following section. In this context, the factors are either an individual variable or an interaction of two or more variables that will affect the likelihood that a certain combination of variables will produce the outcome in the dependent variable that you are examining.

11.5 What Do the Results Mean?

The two statistical packages we have been discussing present the output in a somewhat different format, as do other specialized subroutines or programs written for log linear analysis. The important elements in data analysis that we would like you to see and use are available on all of them, however. The important parts of the output for your interpretation are the observed and expected frequencies in each cell, the goodness-of-fit statistics and associated probabilities, and the estimated parameters of your specified model and their probabilities. We will discuss each of these sections of the results of the analysis with the data on problem pregnancies used in our example. As you will remember, we have decided to use the decision on whether to place the baby for adoption or not, a nominal dichotomy, as our dependent, response, or criterion variable.

11.5.1 Observed and Expected Frequencies

SPSS-X presents the cell frequencies as they exist in your data (the observed frequencies) and those that would have occurred if the frequencies were strictly what you would expect to see by looking at the row and column totals, the marginals. In addition, SPSS-X presents the residuals for each cell, that is, the difference between the observed and the expected frequencies. SAS gives observed frequencies and the probabilities expected, but not the residuals. If you have not looked at representations of multiple-level crosstabulations before, the output may be somewhat confusing. The instructions or manuals that come with the programs give full explanation of the output. In addition the references at the end of this chapter should be helpful to you. We will not attempt to reproduce the full tables, but Table 11.1 below shows a typical SPSS-X output format for LOGLINEAR frequency tables.

TABLE 11.1 Observed and Expected Frequencies and Residuals in SPSS-X

Factor	Code	OBS Count	EXP Count	Residual
Family	1			
Updown	1			
Teen	1			
Place	1	20.00	5.86	14.14
Place	2	.00	6.66	−6.66
Teen	2			
Place	1	4.00	14.65	−10.65
Place	2	26.00	16.65	9.351
Updown	2			
Teen	1			
Place	1	16.00	6.66	9.35

The reason for the indentation on succeeding lines of the column headed Factor and the column headed Code is that they represent different levels of cells. The line that begins with Family and with Code 1 has no observed or expected frequencies on it because we are not interested simply in how many people do or do not have family support. Presumably we know that already. The first line on which we have frequencies is the fourth line, the one with a Code 1 for the variable Place, that is, those who did place their babies. But the way the table is displayed indicates that these are women who had family support (Code 1 on Family), lived in the urban area (Code 1 on Updown) and were teenagers (Code 1 on Teen). The next line also has frequencies and it indicates those women who had Code 1 on all the variables above except that they did not place their babies (Code 2 on Place). We then went to the second value on Teen, a Code 2 for those who were not adolescents but for whom all the other codes than teen were 1s. The next two lines are the number of nonteens who placed and who didn't place. This process continues until all possible cell-frequency values are displayed. The EXP Count

TABLE 11.2 FUNCAT Procedure Frequencies in SAS

Response: Place						Response Levels = 2
	Design			Frequencies		
Sample	Updown	Family	Teen	1	2	Total
1	1	1	1	20	0	20
2	1	1	2	4	26	30

column displays expected frequencies for all of those categories for which we have observed frequencies. The Residual column simply subtracts the expected frequencies
from the observed frequencies.

You have probably noticed that we had no cases in the
cell for urban women who were teens but did not place
their babies. That's the reality of these data, though un-
likely in practice. Does this cause us an empty cell problem and mess up our analysis? No, it doesn't. The place
where empty cells are a problem is in the *expected frequencies,* not in the observed. Indeed, this difference is the stuff
of which statistical significance may be made.

SAS presents this section of the output somewhat differently. As you can see in Table 11.2, each combination of
possible values is presented as a sample, and listed hor-
izontally. This may be easier to read for many of us, but it
does not present the expected frequencies and residuals in
the same table.

Table 11.2 presents the frequencies shown in Table 11.1
in a much more compact format but it presents probabilities in a separate table. Either one is usable if you take time
to understand and practice reading them.

11.5.2 Significance and Goodness of Fit

The next part of the output we'll look at is the significance
statistics for goodness of fit. In other words, how well does

the model you have proposed fit the relationships in the data? Remember the model that we proposed in the sample programs examined not only the effects of individual variables, but also the effects of the interactions among several variables on the observed frequencies. In terms of our current data, it asked if being a teen mother, living downstate, and having family support has a joint effect on the decision to place the baby for adoption that is greater or different than the effect of any one of those things alone. This is the part of the analysis that you cannot do with traditional chi-square techniques alone.

The SPSS-X program we have shown you gives an over-all likelihood ratio chi-square statistic, or a Pearson chi-square statistic, and the probability associated with it, which is significant for the model proposed. SAS, on the other hand, gives us not only the summary chi-square statistics, but also the contribution and significance of each of the elements in the model. This is very useful for the process of perfecting the model by continuing to refine it. In the output produced by this SAS statement, some of the variables and some of the interactions proposed contribute significantly to the model and some did not. The next step would be to look at the significance levels of those elements and remove those that do not contribute significantly from the model. Each program then does the iterations, or recomputations of the data based on the observed marginal totals, to obtain the best possible model using the specifications you have stated. The results of the model-fitting in the program specified in SAS above are in Table 11.3.

As you can see, the only individual variable that has maintained a significant relationship is being an adolescent. The two interaction effects that are significant at probabilities less than .05—Updown by Family by Teen and Family by Teen—both include the extremely powerful variable of being an adolescent and may owe their power to that. If this were your data, it would be appro-

TABLE 11.3 Significance of Fitted Model

Source	DF	Chi-Square	Probability
Intercept	1	1.15	.28
Updown	1	2.50	.11
Family	1	0.32	.57
Teen	1	19.82	.0001
Updown*Family*Teen	1	7.70	.0055
Updown*Family	1	.17	.68
Updown*Teen	1	.22	.64
Family*Teen	1	5.13	.0235

priate to drop the nonsignificant variables and keep the significant interactions and rerun the model to see if you can improve the overall fit.

11.5.3 What Do Parameter Estimates Mean?

The last section of the output that we will examine is the *parameter estimates* portion, which can give us a regression-like interpretation with the coefficients produced. After the iteration has concluded at a level that satisfies the criteria you have specified (in this case we have allowed the default values in both programs to stand), it produces parameter estimates for each variable and interaction specified in our model that will give us an idea of the relative influence of each of these elements or factors. The SPSS-X manual states that multiplying these parameter estimates by 2 allows us to use them in a regression-like equation, using the positive value of the doubled coefficient for cases with a value of 1 on the variable and the negative value for the cases with a value of 2. As in a regression equation, this would allow us to substitute the values of each variable in an individual case for that variable in an equation. The sum of the equation would then be the odds of that case reaching a given score on the dependent or response variable. In the case of the data we are using, the equation would give the odds on that girl or

TABLE 11.4 Parameter Estimates and Probabilities

Effect	Parameter	DF	Estimate	Chi-square	Prob
Intercept	1	1	−.179	1.15	.28
Updown	2	1	.264	2.50	.11
Family	3	1	−.095	0.32	.57
Teen	4	1	.745	19.82	.0001
Updown*Family*Teen	5	1	.464	7.70	.0055
Updown*Family	6	1	.068	.17	.685
Updown*Teen	7	1	−.078	.22	.641
Family*Teen	8	1	−.379	5.13	.023

woman placing her baby for adoption, given what we know about her age, family support, and whether she lives up or downstate.

Since this procedure is based on using logs, the parameter estimates are expressed in logs, and the odds produced by doubling the parameter estimates and using them in the equation are also in logs. To use the more interpretable anti-logs, which are the conversion to the number scales more familiar to most of us, you can look in a table or perform the calculations. It helps if you have a mathematician or engineer handy to help you with this. The parameter estimates produced by our model data are shown in Table 11.4.

As you can see, the parameters maintain the same relationships shown in Table 11.3 with the chi-squares on each factor. That is, most of the significance remains in being an adolescent, and the most significant interaction effects are from the presence or absence of family support and whether the girl was from the city or downstate.

11.6 Final Comments on Log Linear Analysis

Cross-classification techniques are numerous and versatile and becoming more so. Recently, there has been an explosion of interest in them and development and refinement of them. We have deliberately placed log linear analysis at the end of the chapters on techniques, since concepts used in regression, analysis of variance, and factor analysis aid in understanding its application and its interpretation.

This is just a once-over-lightly treatment for those of you who have neither extensive training nor experience in advanced statistical analysis but have a project or question in which you are interested in discovering relationships between characteristics in your data. Whether you are a doctoral or master's student working on a thesis, an agency administrator trying to decide what services to offer or where to offer them, or a clinician attempting to draw conclusions from your experience with clients, log linear analysis may be useful to you. If you have the time and interest, read further on the topic in the books we list below and try different models from the computer manuals with your data. It will take some effort, but it should be well worth it.

One of the most useful early publications on this technique was written by Yvonne Bishop, Stephen Fienberg, and P. W. Holland (1975). H. T. Reynolds (1976, 1977) also has a clear and complete explanation. His 1976 publication is probably more useful for those of you who are not mathematically oriented.

CHAPTER 12

Two Case Studies

In this chapter, we will discuss two research projects in which we have been involved. Going through the problems we encountered in data analysis in each of these situations and the logic we used to solve them may be of some help to you in thinking through the problems in your own studies. What we think is the unique contribution of this book is to make a distinction between statistics and data analysis, terms often used interchangeably. There are a multitude of excellent books on statistics, including all the statistical techniques we have discussed. Most of them have more technical specificity and are more complete in their exposition of the mathematics involved in computing the tests.

In this book and in the case studies in this chapter, we are attempting to show data analysis as an integral part of the research process, one that requires the same knowledge of your subject matter, your research question, and your field as did any step in your project. A good job of data analysis requires that connection between your subject knowledge and your statistical technique. We have seen people with obviously comprehensive knowledge of their area of study and brilliant use of theory do totally inadequate or totally invalid statistical analysis because they do not understand that data analysis requires just as much expertise as does mastery of subject matter.

These case examples will show some typical problems and how we thought them through—which is not the only way; you may be able to think them through differently or better.

12.1 Evaluating a Child-Abuse Treatment Project

This study is fairly typical of many in which we become involved in that we did not know the full extent of the methodological problems when we began. It was an after-the-fact evaluation of a large child-abuse project that had received three years of federal funding (DiLeonardi, 1979). The researchers were told that research had been a goal from the beginning and that a great deal of data had been collected specifically for research purposes. Their mandate was to do something with the data that would provide some evaluation of the effectiveness of the project's approach—the staff and board firmly believed it had been effective—and to learn whatever else was to be gleaned from the data about the nature of the children and families involved that might help in screening of future cases. Some of the data analyses were obvious, including looking at changes during treatment and relative costs of service mixes. Others suggested themselves, such as differences between cases that were reported and substantiated as abuse and those that were not substantiated after investigation.

12.1.1 Problems with Missing Data

After the first enthusiastic approach, problems began to appear in the data, some of which could be corrected and some of which could not. Many of you may decide to use all the information you have on clients or programs (or think you have) to do an evaluation or a needs assessment. The first problem that appears is that people providing services normally hate to do paperwork and avoid it at all costs. If everyone who avoids it avoids the same parts of the paperwork, you have no problem; you don't have the data and must exclude it from your analysis. If the missing data occur in some random fashion, however, you have to look at it very carefully and decide if there is enough there to do anything with. (See the section on missing data in Chapter 6 for some suggestions.)

When the researcher started work on the project, it was obvious that some major changes had to be made in the way the data were coded and stored. In the whole sample of 500 cases, there were holes left by missing data that were large enough to drive a truck through. After several depressing days of reading of material, however, it became obvious that much could be salvaged. There was a logical and consistent pattern to some of the missing data. It wasn't there when it didn't need to be. Workers had stopped recording when they were sure the case would not be substantiated. Much of the missing data was from those cases. The solution was obvious. Analyze those cases separately and only make comparisons where sufficient data were available to do so. They were not, after all, the cases in which we were most interested.

It also became obvious that other data were missing when workers were asked to record the same information several times on several forms and felt the information was redundant. After all, anyone who read the file would know what it was. Unfortunately, the computer statistical package was not going to read the narratives in the file. The solution to that was to decide which variables really were asking the same questions, such as "did physical abuse take place?" If they were indeed the same, the program was written so that if one was true, the other was true. Although this meant that we lost some gradations when a variable that had been a scale became a nominal dichotomy, it was better than losing the whole thing, or in some cases, losing the use of the whole case in multivariate techniques.

Sometimes a whole form was missing. This required some thought in setting up the computer file. It had to be written to accommodate different numbers of data cards on each case. This could have been handled by putting in lines that only had a case number and card number, but since the project was paying for computer storage and processing time with real money, this seemed extravagant as well as cumbersome. This is a problem that often occurs in studies of treatment or service programs that have periodic progress reports. You can hardly require that everyone receive the same amount of service in order to keep your data files neat, tempting though that might be. Chapter 2 gives a good example of the way to set up data files to handle this and other such problems.

12.1.2 Changes in Measures Over Time

An additional problem with the data on this project was that in the forms used to measure progress over time, there was a change in the meaning and level of measurement of the variables related to progress. Initially, families or parents were rated on a validated functioning scale used by other projects. In the course of repeated measures over time, some families changed because the father or mother left, divorced, died, or remarried. Some of the individual ratings at Time 3 were on different people than the individual ratings at Time 1. Those cases were eliminated in the coding.

The major problem, however, was that ratings were changed; for example, at first, the families' ability to manage money was measured on a scale from one to nine, but in later questionnaires, they were rated simply on whether their ability to manage money was better, the same, or worse. If the same scale had been used throughout the program, we could simply have subtracted Time 1 scores from Time 3 scores to see if there was improvement. With the better-worse type of score with no grounding information, we had no idea if there had been real change, and if so, how much. We also had no way of knowing if, when Time 2 and Time 4 both said better and Time 3 said worse, there was any difference between the intake ratings and the closing ratings. All we could do was count the percentage of cases in which there was a rating of better at the end and hope that it meant something real.

The social workers were asked to rate a very large number of variables at the beginning of service after the investigation. It was obviously too much to do, and many families had no problems in some of the areas to be rated. This was useful information in developing problem profiles, but pointless to continue to record month after month. Sometime during the project, the workers rebelled and were allowed to rate only the three most important problems. Unfortunately, the problems that were most important often changed from one time to the next, but they were rated better, the same, or worse even if there were no previous rating for comparison.

12.1.3 Is Using Existing Data Worth It?

With all the problems listed above, why didn't we just throw in the towel and walk away? This project had collected so much data and so much of it was of such good quality that the analysis was definitely worthwhile. Many of our solutions are described above. Others are part of the careful logical process we have been describing throughout the book. For the important variables of existence, severity, and type of abuse, our decision to accept information as valid for more than one form even if it existed only on one came after doing correlations between the two forms in all cases where they were both present, and after establishing reliability at .90 or better. This decision was strengthened by reading the narratives in a good portion of the cases to seek substantiation of the ratings where one was missing.

This process of using what you have to compensate for what you don't have is the key to working with existing data. The only caveat we would offer is be sure not to allow enthusiasm or wishful thinking to lure you into making substitutions not justified by your data.

12.1.4 What Statistics Did We Use?

For the questions of the difference between substantiated and unsubstantiated cases that we mentioned above, much of our analysis was bivariate, using *t*-tests or Mann-Whitney *U* on a variable-by-variable basis because of the problem of missing data in the unsubstantiated cases. Chi-squares were done on the nominal-level variables for the same reasons. For the cost analyses, since many different services were involved, total cost scores for each family were computed by adding them together, and again either *t*-tests for two-group comparisons or analysis of variance for differences between multiple categories were done.

The most interesting analysis to us was that of finding clusters of variables that distinguished physical abuse, sexual abuse, and neglect. We used factor analysis to isolate these variables and checked out our results with discriminant function analysis, successfully classifying over 90% of the cases. With judicious treatment of missing data, we lost fewer than 5% of the substantiated cases for the final analysis.

12.2 Evaluating Client Confidentiality in Police Social Work Settings

This study was a survey of social workers who work in police settings. Its aim was to identify potential problems in protecting the confidentiality of clients. The results were published originally in *Social Work* (Curtis and Lutkus, 1985).

Our purpose here is to demonstrate the thinking that went into the statistical data analysis, particularly in the establishment of reliability and the use of factor analysis and the discriminant function.

12.2.1 Respondents

After a pre-test of three face-to-face interviews, questionnaires were sent to 70 police social workers in Illinois. Forty-one questionnaires were returned for a response rate of 58.6%.

Of the 41 respondents, 14 were male, 26 female. One was not identified by sex. Thirty-six had master's degrees, four had bachelor's degrees. The 41 respondents averaged 6.9 years of work experience since receiving their professional degrees. This included an average of 3.8 years as police social workers.

Nearly 100% of the programs represented by the respondents offered brief counseling, crisis intervention, and referral services. Thirty-five (85.4%) provided long-term counseling, defined as 12 sessions or more. The median number of client referrals to each program was 300 per year. The majority of those referrals were law violators for 22 of the respondents. Eighteen (43.9%) worked in settings with less than two full-time social workers, while 23 (56.19%) had two or more full-time social workers. Twenty-four or 58.5% had offices located within the police building itself. The salaries of 13 (31.7%) were paid directly by police departments, 23 (56.1%) by the local government, 1 by a governmental grant, and 4 (9.8%) by a private social service agency.

12.2.2 Univariate and Bivariate Analysis

A standard bivariate analysis was conducted similar to the procedures we outlined in Chapter 4. That analysis revealed the following.

- Differences in attitudes toward and perceptions of problems with confidentiality were not related to demographic variables such as age of the respondent or gender.

- There was wide variation between respondents in terms of identification with police goals and practices and in terms of attitudes about the kinds of information considered confidential and the circumstances under which it was considered appropriate to share information with the police.
- There was a fairly strong correlation between length of service as a police social worker and identification with police goals and practices.

Let us look at some of the key variables that emerged from the preliminary analysis. When the respondents were asked to whom they considered themselves most responsible in their roles as professionals, 28 (70%) replied their clients, 9 (22.5%) their profession, and 3 (7.5%) their police departments. Thirty-nine ranked their clients either first or second in terms of professional responsibility, while 13 ranked their police departments similarly.

Respondents were asked to respond to a series of Likert type scales with values ranging from (0) Never to (5) Always regarding the kinds of information they considered confidential. The items included Developmental History, Homosexuality, Psychiatric Hospitalization, Current Drug Usage, Past Drug Usage, Homicidal Threats, Suicidal Threats, Having Been Raped, Having Committed Rape, Child Abuse, Alcoholism, Past History of Alcoholism, Having Had an Abortion, Current Law-Violative Behavior, and Past Law-Violative Behavior. Personal information such as developmental history tended to be confidential. Law-violative behavior tended not to be confidential.

Attitudes toward confidentiality were also determined by asking respondents to read four analogs derived from actual, although disguised, police social work cases and then describe how they would have acted under the same circumstances. The first analog they responded to is seen in Figure 12.1.

Eight, or 19.5%, said they would tell the police about

You are seeing a teenage boy in counseling at the police station. He is not psychotic. During a session he reveals that he has stolen some tapes from a car and has stored them in his school locker. He is apologetic about having given you this information, but says that should the police be told, he will no longer trust you and terminate your relationship. If you were the worker in this case, would you inform the police about the tapes?

FIGURE 12.1: Analog One

the tapes; 24, or 58.5%, said they would not, 9 said they were not sure.[1]

Using Telling versus Not Telling the Police as the independent variable, we ran a series of t-tests and learned that workers who would tell the police about the stolen tapes

- tended to feel more responsible professionally to the police than those who would not tell the police about the tapes,
- tended to have worked longer for the police,
- and tended not to consider violent or law-violative behavior confidential.

12.2.3 Reliability

Because the confidentiality items were thought to be important in revealing police social work attitudes and practices and because the items were new and did not represent a validated instrument, it was necessary to establish the reliability of the data. Using Cronbach's alpha, a con-

---

[1]This was an error by the researchers. The analogs were derived from actual incidents, situations in which a police social worker had to make a decision, yet in the questionnaire a "not sure" response was provided.

servative measure of internal consistency, the coefficient of reliability for the 15 items was .90, an excellent result.

The results were very encouraging for two reasons. First, it meant that the scales appeared to be well conceived and that the respondents made their judgments in a rational manner. Secondly, it indicated that a further analysis of the correlation between items was possible, an analysis that was hoped would reveal something about how the respondents made their judgments.

12.2.4 Factor Analysis

One important function of factor analysis is to search for underlying constructs that explain why certain variables are related to one another. In this case, we wanted to know if the variation in the individual confidentiality items would reveal how the police social workers made decisions about what was confidential.

This was a perfect application for factor analysis. The data was reliable, it was strong enough to be treated as interval level, and there was no need to designate any variable as independent or dependent. There was only one problem: not enough cases. According to the standards in this book, 41 subjects were not enough for a multivariate technique that would correlate 15 variables. It was decided to go ahead anyway, hoping that the findings would be clear enough to justify the procedure. We think they were. The results can be seen in Table 12.1.

We learned that the respondents tended to differentiate between the more confidential historical information (60% of the total variance under Factor 1) and the less confidential violent and law-violative information (24.1% of the variance under Factor 2). Notice that Committed Rape loaded on both factors. This may have resulted because the time of the rape was not specified; it could have been a recent incident or one long past. The

TABLE 12.1 Factor Loadings of 15 Areas of Confidentiality

	Factor 1	Factor 2
	History Construct	*Violence Construct*
Developmental History	.78	
Homosexuality	.66	
Psychiatric Hospitalization	.82	
Drug Usage	.86	
Past Drug Usage	.81	
Physical Threats		.87
Suicidal Threats		.87
Victimized by Rape	.62	
Committed Rape	.48	.40
Child Abuse		.66
Alcoholism	.79	
Past Alcoholism	.90	
Having Had an Abortion	.58	
Current Law Violation	.57	.40
Past Law Violation	.61	

loading of Current Law Violation is more difficult to explain. The dual location of both variables may express ambivalence within the group about revealing any information at all.

In this example, most of the loadings on Factor 1 are characteristics about the client's history or past experience such as psychiatric hospitalizations, homosexuality, or developmental history. The highest loading is on past alcoholism. For this reason the authors called this factor "history."

This is not to mislead you into thinking that factor analysis names the constructs for you. That is a matter of interpretation based on scrutinizing the factor loadings. It might also be reasonable to label Factor 2 a law-violative or high-risk construct.

TABLE 12.2 Telling the Police about the Stolen Tapes: Variables Entered

Variable	Wilk's Lambda	Significance	Between Groups	
Length	.60799	.0005	1	2
Violence	.56940	.0012	1	2

12.2.5 Discriminant Function Analysis

Would it be possible to create a model for predicting who would tell the police about the tapes, using the three key predictor variables identified in the previous analyses? The model was set up in the following manner. Telling the Police Versus Not Telling the Police about the stolen tapes was chosen as the classification variable. Originally, there were three predictor variables. They were

- length of experience as a police social worker,
- attitudes toward violence as confidential information, a variable transformation derived from summing the values of all five variables under Factor 2, the aforementioned violence or law-violative construct, and
- a rank-order assessment of professional identification.

The third variable was dropped from the analysis when its contribution was found to be not significant. Length of experience was determined to be the greatest contributor to predicting group membership followed by attitudes toward violence as confidential information. The results can be seen in Table 12.2.

The classification results can be seen in Table 12.3. The longer the social worker worked for the police, the more likely he or she was to tell the police about the stolen tapes. Those who would tell the police averaged 5.7 years as police social workers, while those who would not tell averaged 2.9 years. Those who would tell the police felt

TABLE 12.3 Telling the Police about the Stolen Tapes: Classification Results

Actual Group	N	Predicted Group Membership	
		1	2
1 (Yes)	8	4	4
		50.0%	50.0%
2 (No)	24	2	22
		8.3%	91.7%

Percent of Cases Correctly Classified: 81.25%

more strongly that violent and law-violative behavior was not confidential.

They had an average response of 1.11 on the five variables that made up the violence construct. Recall that a value of 0 meant Never Confidential on a scale from 0 to 5. The average for the other group was 2.11. Although the computer had more trouble with Group 1, the overall classification result of 81.25% was very strong, especially one derived from real data.

Because of the small N and the second predictor variable resulting from Likert scales, interval-level data was not assumed. The METHOD = MAHAL option in the SPSS-X procedure DISCRIMINANT was used in the above analysis. The default procedure did an even better job, misclassifying only four out of 32 cases for a correct classification result of 87.5%.

The findings revealed a growing identification with police goals and practices among those workers with greater tenure in police settings.

CHAPTER 13

Statistical Data Analysis and "Good Enough" Results

We cannot restrain ourselves from saying a few final words. The two very different case examples from the previous chapter were chosen from among the many studies we have conducted or have been associated with in our professional careers in order to illustrate the thinking involved in a project from its design through its final analysis and statement of conclusions. Most published research cannot devote enough space to explain the many decisions that had to be made during the study process. Textbooks sometimes lead one to think that research proceeds only under strict laboratory conditions and, when such conditions are not possible, the study is not worthwhile or the results are suggestive at best. If those textbooks were correct and research was limited to the laboratory, there would be no need for statistics. Statistics use probability as a substitute for laboratory controls.

In the real world there are always problems with missing data, attrition of research subjects, inadequate measures, as well as things all of us together would never anticipate or plan for adequately. The material we have presented in this book is intended to help you deal with these problems in a professional manner. Missing data do not mean you cannot use what you have. A small response rate from a survey does not mean you are restricted to a mere description of those responses. We hope that your knowledge of the subject matter, combined with the techniques we have presented in this book, will maximize what you can derive from a statistical data analysis.

If you have received the impression that the application of statistics to human behavior necessitates stacking judgment upon judgment and making compromise upon compromise, then you have understood our approach to statistical data analysis. We ask only that you think about those judgments, acknowledge those compromises, and remember that a "good enough" result is the best anyone can hope for.

Such is the case when the most stringent controls are imposed on a research design. Consider the classical field experiment, for example. Supposing it were possible to randomly assign subjects to two groups so that those two groups were equivalent statistically on all measurable variables. Then one group receives a treatment while the other serves as a control. Assume there is no contact between the experimental group members and the control group members during the course of the treatment. At follow-up the treatment group tests higher than the control group on some predetermined outcome measure. It is then inferred that the treatment made the difference.

That difference is measured statistically. If the difference is statistically significant, there is a high probability that the result was due to the treatment as opposed to chance. At some point, however, despite the adherence to scientific procedures, someone has to decide whether or not that high probability was "good enough." To begin with, someone has to decide on the alpha. At what level of statistical significance should the null hypothesis of no difference between the groups be rejected? What is more problematical for the task at hand, a Type I or a Type II error?

Because statistical results can be significant, but at the same time weak, we can argue that various error reduction measures such as the effect size and the explained variance should be taken into account. You would still have to decide on what constitutes a "good enough" error reduction. Effect sizes can be interpreted as small, medium, and large. So back we go to ordinal differences! Judgment upon judgment is required for what was supposed to be an exercise in objective measurement.

There is no solution to this dilemma: one can only try to be reasonable. We hope that you find our view of the real world helpful the next time your numbers are in.

GLOSSARY

Analysis of Variance (ANOVA): a multivariate statistical procedure used for testing the influence of one or more categorical predictor (independent) variables on the variance of one criterion (dependent) variable at the interval level of measurement. Additional predictor variables at the interval level of measurement, which may explain some of the variance in the criterion variable, are called *covariates*.

Area of Rejection: that region of the normal distribution which represents the odds, usually expressed as a percentage, for rejecting the null hypothesis. Also referred to as *alpha*. Alpha is the same thing as a *confidence level*. The *area of acceptance* refers to that region of the normal distribution which represents the odds, usually expressed as a percentage, for accepting the null hypothesis. Also referred to as *beta*.

Association: a kind of relationship, usually between categorical variables, in which the assumption of cause and effect is avoided.

Causal Relationship: a condition in which one variable directly influences another variable.

Central Tendency: data described in terms of commonality or the average observation. The mean, median, and mode are measures of central tendency.

Chi-Square: a statistical test used for categorical crosstabulations in which expected frequencies are compared with observed frequencies. The greater the discrepancy between expected and observed frequencies, the greater probability the results are not due to chance.

Class Widths: the range of a category, especially on a scale. *Class intervals* refer to the range between classes or categories.

Closed-Ended Question: an item on a questionnaire or interview schedule in which the respondent is limited to a fixed set of answers.

Computer Files: a general term for blocks of information stored electronically. *Input files* contain information ready to be processed. In statistical data processing, input files usually contain either raw data or programs that process raw data. These programming files are also called *control files* or sometimes *data definition files*. *Output files* contain information that has already been processed and/or is ready to be displayed, printed, or stored again. In statistical data processing, output files are used to display the results of statistical procedures. These files may have a job number as opposed to a name. Another important kind of output file is the *saved file*. It contains information that has been read, defined, and formatted by a statistical package such as SAS or SPSS-X, then stored for future use.

Concurrent Validity: evidence that measurements are truthful derived from results that appear to be logical; for example, survey results that show income correlating with educational achievement.

Continuous Variable: a characteristic, trait, or descriptor in which (1) the individual values are ordered and (2) the intervals between those values can be measured precisely.

Correlation: a kind of relationship in which values fluctuate or covary with one another; for example, as values increase in one variable, they increase in another variable (*positive correlation*) or decrease in another variable (*negative correlation*).

Crosstabulation: a way of displaying data on two or more variables in matrix form; that is, in tables with rows and columns.

Data Set: all the collected information. In computer analysis, data properly formatted for storage.

Data Deletion: the removal of data from a statistical data analysis due to missing information. In *listwise deletion,* an entire case is dropped when any data derived from the variables under analysis are found missing. In *pairwise deletion,* only those correlations between variables with missing data are dropped from the analysis.

Data Reduction: a kind of statistical shorthand. The use of statistical techniques such as factor analysis to reduce the number of variables in an analysis and, at the same time, identify variables important to the analysis.

Data Transformation: the process of changing the structure of data by using techniques which, for example, enhance the level of measurement, reclassify or combine variables in order to create new variables, or substitute values (such as the mean) for missing information.

Dependence: the existence of a relationship in which one characteristic affects another.

Dependent Variable: in a causal relationship, the characteristic that is influenced by the *independent variable*. Not to be confused with *dependence*.

Descriptive Statistics: measurements used to summarize data derived from a known number of subjects. The mean, median, mode, range, standard deviation, and variance are descriptive statistics.

Difference: a kind of relationship in which two samples are not equal statistically.

Discrete Variable: a characteristic, trait, or descriptor in which (1) the individual values are mutually exclusive and (2) the intervals between individual values cannot be measured.

Discriminant Function Analysis: a special case of multiple regression analysis in which the criterion variable, usually referred to as the classification variable, is nominal-level data. Multiple predictor (independent) variables at the interval level of measurement are tested for their ability to predict categorical membership in the classification variable.

Discriminant Validity: evidence that measurements are truthful derived from the absence of results that do not appear to be logical; for example, survey results that do not show that height correlates with educational achievement.

Distribution: all the values in a sample usually sorted into categories or, when appropriate, rank ordered.

Dummy Variable: the treating of nominal-level data as ratio-level data by transforming discrete categories into *none/some scales*. The aim is to enhance the statistical power of nominal-level data.

Eigenvalue: a mathematical property of a matrix representing a certain proportion of the variance within that matrix. Eigenvalues are also called *characteristic roots*.

Explained Variance: a measure, expressed as a percentage, of the extent to which the values of one or more variables determine or account for the values of another variable. Whereas statistical significance measures the probability that a relationship between variables is real as opposed to chance, explained variance measures the strength of statistical relationships.

Factor Analysis: a multivariate statistical technique at the interval level of measurement which identifies commonalities between variables in terms of underlying, hypothetical constructs called *factors*. *Confirmatory* factor analysis tests assumptions about the number and influence of factors within the underlying structure of data. *Exploratory* factor analysis attempts to reveal underlying factors within the data without prior specification of the number or influence of the factors.

Factor Loadings: in factor analysis, correlations, ranging in value from –1.00 to 1.00, between individual observed variables and the underlying factors.

Factor Matrix: in factor analysis, a map of correlations between observed variables and the underlying factors.

Fisher's Exact Test: a substitute for the chi-square test used when more than 20% of the cells in a crosstabulation have expected frequencies less than a value of 5.

Frequency Distribution: a table listing the number of times a particular value occurs. The individual values are called *frequencies*.

Graphic Displays: visual aids used to enhance the meaning and impact of data. *Bar charts* use variable length, horizontal lines or figures to represent frequencies or percentages. *Histograms* use vertical lines or figures. *Pie charts* divide circles into proportional sections that represent frequencies or percentages.

Groupwise Comparisons: comparisons of sample means between sub-groups; for example, the average salaries between men and women. In *pairwise comparisons* only two samples are compared—for example, average salaries at two points in time.

Homoskedasticity: consistent variance in a linear relationship, one of the assumptions underlying the appropriate use of multiple regression analysis. Inconsistent variance is called *heteroskedasticity*.

Hypothesis: a proposition linking two or more characteristics. For the sake of statistical logic, a proposed linkage or relationship is commonly called an *alternative hypothesis*. The negation of such a linkage or relationship is called a *null hypothesis*.

Inclusion Method: the introduction of predictor (independent) variables into a multiple regression procedure. In *hierarchical inclusion,* the number and ordering of predictor variables is specified and then tested for statistical significance and for explained variance. *Stepwise inclusion* is a more exploratory technique. The computer analyzes the relative strengths of a random list of predictor variables and then sorts them for output from the most influential to the least.

Independence: the absence of a relationship.

Independent Variable: the causal characteristic, the variable that affects the outcome. Not to be confused with *independence*.

Interval-Level Measurement: a list or scale of numerical values that are (1) rank ordered and (2) continuous; that is, the distance between each value is of equal and measurable length.

Job Control Language (JCL): system dependent instructions to a computer that are required for data processing.

Kendall's Tau: a non-parametric statistical test of correlation; preferable to Spearman's rho when the data contain many duplicate values.

Lambda: a statistical test used in categorical crosstabulations which measures the probability that membership in a row category predicts membership in a column category (or vice versa).

Levels of Measurement: a way of looking at numbers in terms of the (1) degree of specificity and (2) amount of information they contain.

The concept is especially useful when applied to scaling. There are four levels of measurement; *nominal, ordinal, interval,* and *ratio.*

Likert Scale: an ordinal-level measure of some characteristic, often an attitude or judgment, in which the rank-ordered responses are assumed to represent continuous data, thereby enhancing the power of the measurement. Named after R. Likert.

Linearity: a condition in which relationships among variables can be expressed as a straight line. Linearity is one of the assumptions underlying the appropriate use of multiple regression analysis.

Loglinear Analysis: a multivariate statistical technique for identifying relationships between more than two variables at the nominal level of measurement.

Mean: a simple average. The sum of the values for each observation divided by the number of observations.

Measure of Sampling Adequacy (MSA): in factor analysis, a statistic that measures the relationship of partial correlations to simple correlations. An MSA of less than .50 indicates that at least one variable is not representing adequately some underlying dimension in the data.

Median: the mid-point of a distribution. The value that represents a point where half the observations fall below and half fall above.

Mode: the category or value in a distribution with the largest number of observations. *Bi-modal* distributions contain two categories or values with the largest number of observations.

Multi-Collinearity: in multiple regression analysis and other multivariate procedures, the high correlation among predictor (independent) variables. The results of multivariate statistical procedures are confounded by multi-collinearity.

Multivariate Statistics: procedures that analyze the relationships between more than two variables. Examples include multiple correlations such as factor analysis, multiple associations such as log linear analysis, and procedures that use multiple predictor (independent) variables to account for values in a single criterion (dependent) variable such as multiple regression analysis, analysis of variance, and discriminant function analysis.

Nominal-Level Measurement: a list of discrete categories that make up a scale in name only. No individual category can be ranked as higher or lower than the other categories.

None/Some Scale: a special case of nominal-level data in which one category is assigned a value of 1 which represents the presence of some characteristic and a value of 0 which represents the absence of that characteristic. The resulting scale is *dichotomous,* containing only two values.

Non-Parametric Statistics: measurements in which assumptions about the nature of underlying data are not required.

Normal Distribution (Curve): a theoretical arrangement of values in which the *mean, median,* and *mode* are equal and in which distances from the mean may be measured in standard units.

Oblique Rotation: an operation to find the simple structure in a factor analysis in which the assumption of orthogonality (independence) is not imposed. The resulting factors, therefore, are assumed to correlate with one another. In *orthogonal rotation,* it is assumed that the factors are not correlated and are, therefore, independent of one another.

One-Tail/Two-Tail Statistical Tests: the tails refer to the extreme ends of a distribution. *One-tail* tests hypothesize direction in a relationship; for example, men will outperform women on an exam. *Two-tail* tests do not; for example, there will be a difference in exam scores between men and women.

Open-Ended Question: an item on a questionnaire or interview schedule in which the respondent is allowed to answer with a qualitative, narrative statement.

Ordinal-Level Measurement: a list of discrete categories that can be rank ordered.

Parameter Estimates: in log linear analysis, the estimated values of the interactions between variables after iteration as postulated in any given model.

Parametric Statistics: measurements in which certain assumptions can be made about the nature of the underlying data. The data are assumed to represent known boundaries or parameters, e.g., interval or ratio-level measurement, normal distribution. When these assumptions are met, inferences can be made about populations from which the data were drawn.

Partial Correlation: a technique used for detecting spurious or overlooked correlations that result from powerful sub-group influences.

Pearson's r (Pearson's Product Moment Correlation Coefficient): the most commonly used parametric statistical test of correlation.

Population: in surveys and polls, all the subjects from which a sample is chosen.

Power: the extent to which data can represent the real world. *Statistical power* refers to the extent to which statistical tests can detect relationships in the real world.

Precoded Question: an item on a questionnaire or interview schedule in which responses are assigned numerical values for easy computer input.

Predictive Relationship: a condition in which one variable has a measurable effect on another variable.

Principal Components Analysis: in factor analysis, a technique that develops linear, orthogonal combinations of the observed variables so that the first principal component represents the largest amount of variance, the second represents the next largest amount of variance, and so on.

Probability: the odds that a measurement is accurate.

Random Assignment: a method for choosing subjects, usually in a field experiment, in which each subject has an equal chance of being assigned to various conditions or treatments.

Random Selection (Sampling): a method of choosing subjects from a population in which each subject has an equal chance of being chosen.

Range: in a distribution the distance from the lowest value to the highest.

Ratio-Level Measurement: a list or scale of numerical values that (1) are rank ordered, (2) are continuous, and (3) contain somewhere on the scale a value of absolute zero.

Relationship: a general term meaning a linkage or co-existence between variables.

Reliability: stability of measurement. The ability of an instrument to achieve the same result over repeated measures. *Inter-rater reliability* refers to consistent measurement between judges. *Inter-item reliability* refers to the correlation of conceptually related measurements.

Residual: in multiple regression analysis, the shortest distance from any data point to the regression line. An *outlier* is an unusual data point at great distance from the regression line. Outliers threaten the assumption of linearity.

Scatterplot: a visual representation of data points, especially correlations. Scatterplots are useful in confirming visually the existence of linear relationships, identifying outliers, and checking for homoskedasticity.

Scree Plot: in factor analysis, a graph of the eigenvalues showing their relative magnitude. The point on the plot where the values stop descending and level off is a visual criterion for the selection of factors to be used in further analysis.

Skewness: in a frequency distribution, a departure from normality, i.e. perfect symmetry. When the mean, median, and mode are not equal, a distribution is said to be skewed.

Spearman's Rho: the most commonly used non-parametric statistical test of correlation.

Standard Deviation: a measure of dispersion, the extent to which individual values deviate from the average.

Statistical Significance: the extent to which a relationship between two or more variables is real as opposed to chance.

T-Test (Student's T-Test): a statistical test used for comparing the difference between the means of two samples or the mean of one sample and its population.

Validity: the extent to which a measurement is truthful. *Internal validity* refers to measuring what one intends to measure. *External validity* refers to the extent to which a measurement may be generalized.

Variability: the extent to which values will deviate from the average observation. Also called *dispersion*. The range, standard deviation, and variance are measures of variability or dispersion.

Variable: a characteristic, trait, or descriptor that has more than one value, i.e., that varies. An *independent* variable is a causal characteristic. A *dependent* variable is influenced by independent variables. Because (1) the words independent and dependent imply cause and effect and (2) statistics do not confirm the existence of cause and effect, *predictor variable* can be substituted for independent variable and *criterion variable* can be substituted for dependent variable.

Variance: the standard deviation squared. A measure of dispersion difficult to interpret, but important in the calculation of many statistics.

Z-Scores: transformed values measured in standard deviation units derived from distributions that are not normal for the sale of measuring (1) distances from the mean or (2) probability.

BIBLIOGRAPHY

Bibby, J. "The General Linear Model—A Cautionary Tale." *The Analysis of Survey Data. Vol. 2: Model Fitting,* edited by C. A. O'Muircheartaigh and Clive Payne. New York: Wiley, 1977.

Bishop, Yvonne, Fienberg, Stephen, and Holland, P. W. *Discrete Multivariate Analysis: Theory and Practice.* Cambridge: MIT Press, 1975.

BMDP Biomedical Computer Programs. Berkeley: University of California Press, 1977.

Cohen, Jacob. *Statistical Power Analysis for the Behavioral Sciences.* New York: Academic Press, 1977.

Curtis, Patrick A., and Lutkus, Anita M. "Client Confidentiality in Police Social Work Settings." *Social Work* 30 (July–August 1985).

Curtis, Patrick A., Rosman, Marshall D., and Pappenfort, Donnell. "Development of an Instrument for Measuring Psychosocial Assessment in Clinical Child Welfare." *Child Welfare* 53 (July–August 1984).

DiLeonardi, Joan W. *The MAPS Project Report.* Chicago: Voluntary Interagency Association, 1979.

Hartwig, Frederick, and Dearing, Brian E. *Exploratory Data Analysis.* Beverly Hills: Sage, 1979.

Horowitz, Gideon. *Sadistic Statistics.* Wagner, N.J.: Avery Publishing Group, 1981.

Kendall, Maurice. *Multivariate Analysis.* New York: Hafner Press, 1975.

Kerlinger, Fred. *Foundations of Behavioral Research.* New York: Holt, Rinehart and Winston, Inc., 1973.

Kerlinger, Fred, and Pedhazur, E. J. *Multiple Regression in Behavioral Research.* New York: Holt, Rinehart and Winston, 1973.

Kim, Jae-On and Mueller, Charles. *Introduction to Factor Analysis: What It Is and How to Do It.* Beverly Hills: Sage, 1978.

Kim, Jae-On and Mueller, Charles. *Factor Analysis: Statistical Analysis and Practical Issues.* Beverly Hills: Sage, 1978.

Klecka, William. *Discriminant Analysis.* Beverly Hills: Sage, 1978.

Krijcie, R. J. and Morgan, D. W. "Determining Sample Size for Research Activities." *Educational and Psychological Measurement* 30 (1970).

Reynolds, H. T. *Analysis of Nominal Data.* Beverly Hills: Sage, 1976.

Reynolds, H. T. *The Analysis of Cross-Classifications.* New York: The Free Press, 1977.

Ripple, Lillian. "Motivation, Capacity, and Opportunity as Related to the Use of Casework Service." *Social Service Review* 29 (June 1955).

Ripple, Lillian, Alexander, Ernestina, and Polemis, Bernice. *Motivation, Capacity, and Opportunity.* Social Service Monographs. Chicago: University of Chicago Press, 1964.

SAS User's Guide: Statistics. Cary, N.C.: SAS Institute, 1982.

SPSS-X User's Guide. New York: McGraw-Hill, 1983.

Stevens, S. "On the Theory of Scales of Measurement." *Science* 103 (1946): 677–80.

Tukey, J. W. *Exploratory Data Analysis.* Reading, Mass.: Addison-Wesley, 1977.

INDEX